Good Food Made Simple

HEALTHY

Good Food Made Simple

HEALTHY

Over 140 delicious recipes, 500 colour photographs, step-by-step images and nutritional information

This edition published by Parragon Books Ltd in 2014
LOVE FOOD is an imprint of Parragon Books Ltd

Parragon Books Ltd
Chartist House
15–17 Trim Street
Bath BA1 1HA, UK
www.parragon.com/lovefood

ISBN 978-1-4723-5700-7

Printed in China

New photography by Noel Murphy
New recipes by Christine France
New introduction and note text by Judith Wills
Nutritional analysis by Fiona Hunter

Notes for the Reader
This book uses both metric and imperial measurements. Follow the same units of measurement throughout; do not mix metric and imperial. All spoon measurements are level: teaspoons are assumed to be 5 ml, and tablespoons are assumed to be 15 ml. Unless otherwise stated, milk is assumed to be full fat, eggs and individual vegetables are medium, and pepper is freshly ground black pepper. Unless otherwise stated, all root vegetables should be peeled prior to using.

Garnishes, decorations and serving suggestions are all optional and not necessarily included in the recipe ingredients or method. Any optional ingredients and seasoning to taste are not included in the nutritional analysis. The times given are an approximate guide only. Preparation times differ according to the techniques used by different people and the cooking times may also vary from those given. Optional ingredients, variations or serving suggestions have not been included in the time calculations.

Picture acknowledgements
The publisher would like to thank the following for permission to reproduce copyright material on page 8: Single pea on white plate © amana productions inc./Getty Images and Five food groups © Maximilian Stock Ltd./Getty Images.

Contents

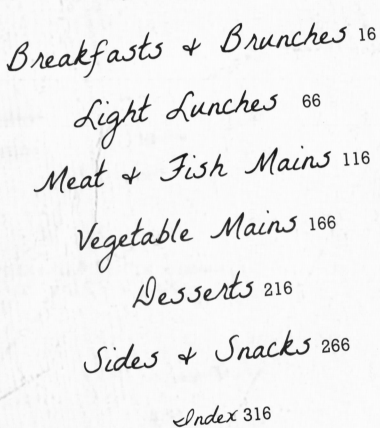

What is a balanced diet?

Most of us have heard the phrase 'a balanced diet' before but it is not always easy to know exactly what this means. What should we be eating on a daily or weekly basis? Below, we will explain what a balanced diet is and what you should be eating regularly to maintain a healthy lifestyle.

A balanced diet means eating a wide variety of foods in the right proportions. It also means consuming adequate calories from what you eat and drink so that you maintain a reasonable weight.

If we can balance the major calorie-providing nutrients, such as carbohydrates, fats and protein, then they should provide all of the other smaller elements of a healthy diet without us having to worry too much about them. These smaller elements are called the 'micro-nutrients' – otherwise known as vitamins, minerals and plant chemical compounds, as well as dietary fibre.

What's on the plate?

The healthy food plate below shows the ideal proportions of food to eat each day (for an average adult).

A balanced diet means eating a wide variety of foods in the right proportions.

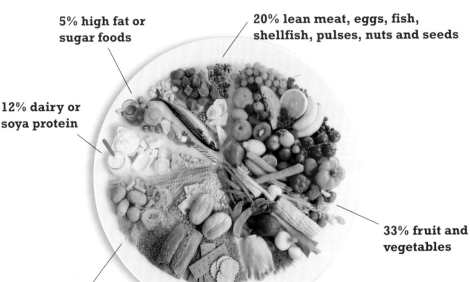

5% high fat or sugar foods

20% lean meat, eggs, fish, shellfish, pulses, nuts and seeds

12% dairy or soya protein

33% fruit and vegetables

30% starchy foods

33% fruit and vegetables: These are the richest providers of many vitamins, plant chemicals and fibre. At least five portions every day are preferable and the ideal balance is two fruits and three vegetables. Try to choose a rainbow of different colours to ensure you get a complete range of nutrients.

30% starchy foods: Starchy foods, such as grains (preferably whole), bread, pasta and root vegetables provide a range of vitamins, minerals, plant chemicals and fibre, as well as the calories we need.

20% lean meat, eggs, fish, shellfish, pulses, nuts and seeds: Try to vary your choices within this section – it is good to eat fish regularly (including oily fish), but also have meals including pulses, such as beans or lentils, or nuts and seeds.

12% dairy or soya protein: This section includes milk, cheese and yogurt, or calcium-fortified soya milk and yogurts. Cream and cream cheeses aren't included as they contain little protein and lots of saturated fat!

5% high fat or high sugar foods: These are what might be called 'junk foods' and should be eaten in very small amounts (or not at all, if possible). This section includes sugar, sugary drinks, cakes, biscuits, pastries and confectionery.

Your recommended amounts

Nutritional experts have established some recommended levels for all of the major and micro-nutrients that make up a balanced diet. These include the nutrients that we need to get in adequate amounts, such as protein, certain fats and carbohydrates, but also maximum levels for those items that we should limit, such as saturated fats, sugar and salt. The chart below is based on those recommendations.

Your healthy diet and food labelling

Nowadays, almost all manufactured food has nutritional information on the label, with the amount of each nutrient per portion usually listed. It also details the percentage of the recommended amount of each nutrient that a portion provides. Keeping an eye on labels is a good way to make sure you stay within healthy limits.

But nutritional guidelines are there as just that – a guide to what, on average, you should be getting in your diet every day. There is no need to worry about reaching the exact figures for each nutrient each day – as long as, over the course of a week, you get a good balance.

This relaxed way of planning your diet means that you can have the occasional treat or day when you want to eat more. Don't feel guilty – all you do is cut back a little on the other days of the week. Food gives you life and health but don't forget, it is also there to be enjoyed – within reasonable limits!

Recommended daily amounts*

	Kcals	Fat	Sat Fat**	Carbs	Sugar**	Protein***	Fibre***	Salt**
Men	2605	95g	30g	350g	120g	55g	24g	6g
Women	2079	76g	20g	275g	90g	45g	24g	6g

*   Based on average adult male and female – individuals may differ.

** Recommended maximum – less may be preferable.

*** Recommended minimum – more may be preferable.

What is healthy food?

A healthy food is one that contains a good level and variety of nutrients, as well as being low in components known to have an adverse effect on us. Most experts also say that a healthy diet is one that contains a high proportion of unprocessed or minimally processed natural foods, especially plant foods.

Most experts say that a healthy diet is one that contains a high proportion of unprocessed, natural foods.

Some of the most important nutrients for health are those that we need only in small amounts, but are essential for good health. These are vitamins, minerals, essential fatty acids and a vast range of plant chemicals, which are the newest stars of the nutrition world.

Vitamins

Vitamins are minute particles that help to protect us from disease and are important in the day-to-day functioning, protection and maintenance of our bodies.

Vitamins that we need regularly but not necessarily every day as they can be stored in the body are:

Vitamin A – for healthy growth, skin and vision, found mainly in meat, dairy produce and eggs. The body can also convert carotenes, found in brightly coloured plant foods, into vitamin A.

Vitamin D – for calcium absorption and other functions, found in oily fish and eggs.

Vitamin E – a powerful antioxidant that helps prevent heart disease, found in nuts, seeds, other plant oils and some other plant foods.

Vitamin K – for normal blood clotting, found in a wide variety of foods.

Vitamins we need daily, ideally, as they cannot be stored in the body are:

Vitamin C – for the immune system, to help iron absorption, and many other roles, such as being an antioxidant. Found in fruits and vegetables.

Vitamin B group – these work together for growth, a healthy nervous system, and food metabolism. Found in meat, fish, pulses, eggs and dairy produce.

Minerals

There are 15 minerals that we need to get from what we eat and drink. The major minerals that we can easily fall short on are:

Calcium – for healthy bones and with several other roles, found in dairy produce, nuts, seeds and dried fruit.

Iron – for healthy blood and transportation of oxygen, found in meat, pulses, whole grains and leafy greens.

Magnesium – for bone density, and a healthy nervous system, heart and muscles, found in nuts, seeds and dairy produce.

Potassium – for regulating blood pressure and for a healthy heart, found in many fruits and vegetables.

Zinc – for a healthy immune system, skin and fertility, found in red meat, shellfish, nuts and seeds.

Selenium – for a healthy immune system, found in nuts, pulses and fish.

Fats in your diet

All fats – at 9 calories per gram – are a concentrated source of energy, but the types of fat we find in our food and their effects on our health can vary considerably.

Saturated fats – These are the fats found in highest amounts in animals fats, such as lard, butter, fatty meats and high-fat dairy produce. Overconsumption is linked with increased blood cholesterol and heart disease.

Trans fats – These occur naturally in foods, such as meat and high-fat dairy produce, but can also occur in processed foods, such as biscuits and cakes. These raise blood cholesterol and are linked to increased risk of heart disease.

Monounsaturated fats – These are found in certain plant foods and their oils, including olive oil, avocados, rapeseed oil and hazelnuts. Regular consumption appears to have a protective effect against both heart disease and some cancers.

Polyunsaturated fats – These are found in a range of plant foods, such as corn oil, sunflower oil, safflower oil, blended vegetable oil, nuts, seeds and processed soft margarines. Whilst this group contains the 'essential fatty acids' (see below) and can help lower blood cholesterol, our intake of polyunsaturated fats tends to be more than adequate.

Essential fatty acids – Within the polyunsaturated group of fats there are two essential fats that the body can't manufacture itself: the omega-6 fat linoleic acid (found in nuts and seeds and their oils) and the omega-3 fat alpha-linolenic acid or ALA (found in flaxseed, flaxseed oil, rapeseed oil and walnut oil). The body can convert ALA to EPA and DHA – two omega-3 fatty acids linked with protection from heart disease and with a variety of other benefits, but EPA and DHA are also found directly in oily fish.

Superfoods

The term 'superfoods' is used to describe foods that have particularly potent health benefits. They may contain a high level of vitamin C or be rich in heart-protecting soluble fibre, such as oats or lentils. But often the term is used for a food that has high levels of plant compounds, which can have a strong antioxidant effect in our bodies. Experts have now found thousands of these compounds – with names such as flavonoids, polyphenols, carotenes, sulphides and glucosinolates – that offer us protection from diseases such as cancer, arthritis and heart disease, and also help everyday wellbeing. Any diet that contains a wide variety of plant foods should be rich in 'superfoods'.

How can I be more healthy?

A balanced and varied diet is crucial to your well-being, but other lifestyle choices can have important roles to play too. It is not only what you eat but also how much you eat that matters, as well as getting enough exercise into your daily routine. It is essential to know how to balance your energy intake – matching how many calories you eat or drink with how many you burn off during exercise. There are several tips you can use to help you achieve this energy balance without too much effort.

It is essential to know how to balance your energy intake – matching how many calories you eat or drink with how many you burn off.

Increase your exercise

Several worldwide studies have shown that many of us put on weight not because we are eating much more than we used to, but because we burn fewer calories through activity. We humans were designed to use our bodies – to walk, to run, to climb – but in the modern world it is easy to do very little. Cars, home appliances, the Internet, TV, office jobs, escalators and lifts all help to keep us sedentary.

Exercise not only helps keep your weight stable (and can actually help you lose weight), it has many other benefits too. It improves sleep patterns and insomnia, helps lift depression, keeps joints supple, improves posture, increases strength and mobility, improves heart and lung health and can even decrease the risk of diabetes.

The best exercise is anything you enjoy doing and that you can do without huge expense or adjusting your life too much. Walking is ideal as it can be fitted in anywhere, is free and every minute counts as exercise. Try taking the stairs not the lift or walking one extra stop instead of taking the bus all the way. But also think about cycling, swimming or even dancing in your sitting room! Try to do at least 30 minutes a day, five days a week.

Think about how you eat

In our busy lives, it is so easy to grab a quick ready meal here and a takeaway there. And if we're hungry between meals, it is so simple to buy a chocolate bar or a bag of crisps.

But, if you want to eat a balanced and varied diet, you need to become more mindful of these

eating patterns and begin making little changes.

If you have been so busy that food has been taking a backseat in your life, think about small ways you can make it more important. For example, try to choose wisely and take more time over shopping, preparation and eating your food. Food is, or should be, a pleasure, not a chore – so use it as a way to be kind to yourself.

Here are some other ideas you might use:

• Set aside 30 minutes or so at the weekend to plan some easy evening meal ideas you might like to try from this book, along with some healthy packed lunches you might take to work and some quick, healthy breakfasts. Then, write your shopping list and enjoy a trip to the local shops to stock up. Home cooking can be a relaxing pleasure and it doesn't have to be difficult. The results will almost always be healthier and tastier than those takeaways!

• When you buy ready-made foods, keep an eye on the labels so that you choose items that will fit in with your exercise levels, calorie and nutrition needs (see page 9).

• Save money – keep an eye on your portion sizes when you cook. It's tempting to make a little extra 'just in case' but only do that if you can make one and freeze one for another day. Research shows that cutting down portion sizes a little at most meals is a great way to lose weight and keep it off.

• Eat regularly. It is better to eat small meals more frequently than to try to 'be good' and have just one big meal, for example. That often leads to bingeing and cravings, as well as making you feel dizzy or headachy. An ideal pattern is breakfast, lunch, a small late afternoon snack and an evening meal. The eating plan on page 15 shows you how your day's menu might look.

• Take time to relax and enjoy your food – chew everything well and really savour it. Research shows you eat less if you do this, rather than using a mealtime to work, read or watch TV.

How do I use this book?

Now that you have a good understanding of what a healthy lifestyle is, you'll want to include many of our recipes in your diet in the weeks and months ahead. Check back to page 9. You will see the chart listing recommended amounts of the major nutrients. Now flick through our recipes and you'll see that each one contains nutritional information, so it is easy to keep a check on whether you're eating too many calories each day, whether you're cutting down enough on, for example, salt, or if you're getting sufficient fibre in your diet.

There is also useful 'flag' information in the top left of each recipe, telling you what particular types of diet each recipe can be used in and/or its special benefits. The flags are:

Super low calorie: This means the recipe is suitable for anyone on a slimming diet. If you pick a low-calorie flagged meal each day for breakfast, lunch and dinner, as well as one flagged snack OR dessert, plus a 250 ml/9 fl oz milk allowance and unlimited salad greens and leafy greens, you will be eating no more than 1,350 calories – a suitable level to lose weight steadily until your target. Make sure you don't eat too few calories though – this would be less than 1,200 calories per day for a woman and less than 1,500 for a man.

Extra low sat fat: This means that the recipe contains less than 4g saturated fat per portion, which is well within the target set by health professionals for those people required to follow a low saturated fat diet.

Wheat, gluten and dairy free: This flag means that the recipe contains no wheat, gluten or dairy and therefore is suitable for people following a diet that excludes any or all of these items.

Fuller for longer: This flag is useful for people on a low-calorie diet, people who tend to get very hungry, very active people, or anyone who has diabetes or its precursor, pre-diabetes (or high blood glucose levels). These recipes are rich in the types of food that help regulate blood glucose. These foods are proteins, healthy fats and certain high-fibre foods low on the Glycaemic Index (an index showing the rate at which different foods are absorbed into the bloodstream). This flag shows that at least 50% of the calories in the recipe should come from nutrients that help you feel fuller for longer.

Low on carbs: These recipes contain low levels of starches and/or sugars (both types of carbohydrate). This flag is useful for people following a low-carbohydrate diet for health reasons or slimming purposes. This flag shows that less than 20% of the calories in this recipe come from carbohydrates.

Protein packed: Recipes flagged with this symbol are high protein and may be especially useful for people who prefer to diet or maintain their weight on a lower-carb, higher-protein regime. High-protein diets can help beat hunger and also speed the metabolic rate (the rate at which you burn calories). They are also useful if you are exercising to build lean tissue muscle. This flag shows that at least 40% of the calories in this recipe come from protein.

Your week's food plan

This plan is suitable for an average woman for weight maintainance. It provides a balance of all the nutrients you need and is also within the guidelines for fat, saturated fat, sugars and salt. So, for example, a meal that's higher in, say, fat (or salt or sugar) will be followed by one that's lower, and so a healthy balance is kept. We suggest that men should add extras, such as bread, potato, pasta, rice, noodles, nuts, seeds and fruit, to add on the further 500 or so calories they need each day.

You can also have 250 ml/9 fl oz skimmed, semi-skimmed or calcium-fortified soya milk every day and don't forget to drink several glasses of water or herbal tea a day. Salad greens and leafy greens are unlimited, as are fresh herbs and spices and lemon juice. The recipes listed in the plan should be taken to be 1 serving of the recipe, unless stated otherwise.

Day One

Breakfast: Apricot & Apple Compote (page 30) with 1 tbsp chopped nuts; 125 ml/4 fl oz low-fat yogurt or soya yogurt; 1 x 40 g/1½ oz slice wholegrain toast with 2 tsp unsalted low-fat spread.
Lunch: Chicken Noodle Bowl (page 82); 1 orange.
Snack: Grazing Mix (page 298); 1 large banana.
Dinner: Chunky Monkfish Hotpot (page 160); 175 g/6 oz mashed potato made with skimmed milk and low-fat spread; 85 g/3 oz steamed broccoli; Coconut Rice Pudding (page 232).

Day Two

Breakfast: Banana Breakfast Shake (page 58); 8 almonds; 1 red-skinned apple.
Lunch: Red Pepper Hummus, Rocket & Artichoke Wraps (page 88).
Snack: 3 Beetroot Brownie Bites (page 306); 125 g/4½ oz low-fat natural yogurt.
Dinner: Polenta Tart (page 190); 1 large bowl mixed leaf salad with 1 tbsp olive oil French dressing; Fluffy Lemon Pot (page 228).

Day Three

Breakfast: Crunchy Brunch Wraps (page 60).
Lunch: Shaker Salad in a Jar (page 76).
Snack: Grazing Mix (page 298); 1 large banana.
Dinner: Braised Soy & Ginger Pork Fillets (page 140); 50 g/1¾ oz (dry weight) wholewheat noodles, cooked; Oaty Plum Bake (page 264); 1 tbsp low-fat natural yogurt.

Day Four

Breakfast: Breakfast Cookie (page 38); 1 large banana.
Lunch: Smoked Mackerel Salad (page 90); 40 g/1½ oz wholegrain bread with 2 tsp unsalted low-fat spread; 1 orange.
Snack: Apple Dip Pots (page 304).
Dinner: Tofu Steak with Fennel & Orange (page 180); Raw Beetroot & Pecan Side Salad (page 270); 50 g/1¾ oz (dry weight) bulgar wheat, cooked; Peach Popovers (page 224).

Day Five

Breakfast: Grape Pancake Stacks (page 36).
Lunch: Wholewheat Spaghetti with Edamame Beans (page 92); 1 large bowl mixed leaf salad with 1 tbsp olive oil French dressing.
Snack: Peanut Dip with Pitta Crisps (page 290).
Dinner: Chickpea & Halloumi Salad (page 200); Vanilla Soufflé Omelette (page 222).

Day Six

Breakfast: Cherry & Almond Muesli (page 28).
Lunch: Brown Rice Lunchbowl (page 100); 1 orange.
Snack: Peanut Dip with Pitta Crisps (page 290) and crudités.
Dinner: Grilled Salmon with Mango & Lime Salsa (page 152); 200 g/7 oz steamed new potatoes; 85 g/3 oz steamed green beans; Golden Polenta Cake (page 236).

Day Seven

Breakfast: Spinach Scramble with Toasted Rye (page 50); 1 banana.
Lunch: Warm Shredded Beef Tabbouleh Salad (page 84).
Snack: Grazing Mix (page 298); 3 Beetroot Brownie Bites (page 306).
Dinner: Tempeh Noodle Bowl (page 194); Apple & Almond Roulade (page 238).

Berry Sunrise Smoothie *18*

Strawberry Yogurt Dip *20*

Spicy Apple Oats *22*

Nectarine Crunch *24*

Apricot Flapjacks *26*

Cherry & Almond Muesli *28*

Apricot & Apple Compote *30*

Cranberry & Seed Muesli *32*

Pumpkin & Pecan Pancakes *34*

Grape Pancake Stacks *36*

Gluten- and Dairy-free Breakfast Cookies *38*

Millet Porridge with Apricot Purée *40*

Courgette Fritters *42*

Sausage & Potato Omelette *44*

Baked Mushrooms with Herb Ricotta *46*

Breakfast Burrito *48*

Spinach Scramble with Toasted Rye Bread *50*

Poached Eggs in Tomato Sauce *52*

Mushrooms on Toast *54*

Red Pepper Booster *56*

Banana Breakfast Shake *58*

Crunchy Brunch Wraps *60*

Wholemeal Muffins *62*

Raw Buckwheat & Almond Porridge *64*

Breakfasts & Brunches

Fuller for longer

Extra low sat fat

Super low calorie

Wheat, gluten & dairy free

Berry Sunrise Smoothie

 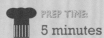 SERVES 1

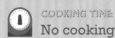 PREP TIME:
5 minutes

COOKING TIME:
No cooking

nutritional information **per serving**

259 kcals, 4g fat, 0.7g sat fat, 46g total sugars, trace salt, 4.5g fibre, 48g carbs, 9.5g protein

For a quick and filling pick-me-up before heading out of the door, this tasty smoothie can't be beaten.

INGREDIENTS

1 banana
55 g/2 oz silken tofu, drained
175 ml/6 fl oz orange juice
200 g/7 oz frozen mixed berries

1. Roughly chop the banana and the tofu into smaller pieces.

2. Place all of the ingredients in a blender on high speed or use a hand-held blender and then process until smooth. Let the smoothie settle for a few seconds and then process again to fully blend.

3. Serve the smoothie immediately in a tall drinking glass.

1

2

2

SOMETHING
DIFFERENT
Try using apple
juice instead of
orange juice for
a change — either
cloudy or smooth
works well.

Strawberry Yogurt Dip

Fuller for longer

Extra low sat fat

Super low calorie

 SERVES 4

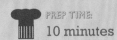 PREP TIME:
10 minutes

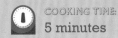 COOKING TIME:
5 minutes

nutritional information per serving	166 kcals, 5g fat, 3g sat fat, 13g total sugars, 0.4g salt, 4g fibre, 24g carbs, 6.5g protein

This beautifully balanced dish is great for slimmers and is rich in fibre, vitamin C and antioxidants.

INGREDIENTS

100 g/3½ oz ripe strawberries, hulled and roughly chopped, plus extra to garnish

1 tbsp icing sugar

200 g/7 oz natural fromage frais

1 tsp lemon juice

4 slices wholemeal bread

2 large pieces of fruit, such as a mango, nectarine or banana, cut into wedges

1. Process the strawberries with the icing sugar in a blender for a few seconds or mash with the sugar using a fork.

2. Combine the mixture with the fromage frais and lemon juice in a bowl. Spoon into a serving dish and chill, if you have time.

3. Toast the bread and cut into fingers. Arrange the fruit as dippers on a plate around the strawberry dip. Garnish the dip with halves of fresh strawberries. Serve immediately, with the toast fingers.

1

2

3

SOMETHING
DIFFERENT
In the winter, you could replace the strawberries with very ripe, chopped pears.

Fuller for longer

Extra low sat fat

Spicy Apple Oats

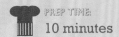 SERVES 6

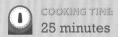 PREP TIME:
10 minutes

COOKING TIME:
25 minutes

nutritional information per serving	300 kcals, 8g fat, 3g sat fat, 26g total sugars, 0.7g salt, 5g fibre, 50g carbs, 9g protein

Healthy porridge oats get a boost of flavour from apples, dried fruit and cinnamon.

INGREDIENTS

2 sprays vegetable oil spray

2 large eggs

150 ml/5 fl oz skimmed milk

50 g/1¾ oz soft light brown sugar

115 g/4 oz apple sauce

1 tsp baking powder

½ tsp salt

½ tsp ground cinnamon

225 g/8 oz porridge oats

2 large, red-skinned apples, cored and diced

70 g/2½ oz dried fruit (raisins, apricots, cranberries, cherries or a combination)

1 tbsp unsalted butter, melted

1. Preheat the oven to 190°C/375°F/Gas Mark 5. Coat a shallow, wide ovenproof dish or 6 x 225-ml/8-fl-oz ramekins with vegetable oil spray.

2. Beat the eggs and milk in a bowl. Add the brown sugar, apple sauce, baking powder, salt and cinnamon and stir until thoroughly mixed. Stir in the oats, apples and dried fruit and mix well.

3. Spoon the mixture into the prepared ovenproof dish (or ramekins), add dots of the butter, and bake in the preheated oven for about 25 minutes or until hot and bubbling. Leave to cool slightly before serving.

BE PREPARED
You can make this dish the day before it is required – leave to cool completely, cover and store in the refrigerator.

Fuller for longer

Extra low sat fat

Nectarine Crunch

 SERVES 3

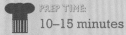 PREP TIME:
10–15 minutes

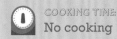 COOKING TIME:
No cooking

nutritional information **per serving**

400 kcals, 11.5g fat, 2.5g sat fat, 44g total sugars, 0.2g salt, 6g fibre, 64g carbs, 15g protein

Serve this crunchy, fruity concoction as a speedily prepared brunch dish. Peaches would be an excellent substitute for nectarines too.

INGREDIENTS

4 nectarines
2 tbsp peach jam
2 tbsp peach juice
175 g/6 oz raisin and nut crunchy oat cereal
300 g/10½ oz low-fat natural yogurt

1. Cut the nectarines in half, then remove and discard the stones. Chop the flesh into bite-sized pieces and reserve a few slices for decoration.

2. Place the jam and peach juice in a bowl and mix together.

3. Place a few of the nectarine pieces in the bottom of three sundae glasses. Top with half of the oat cereal and a spoonful of the yogurt. Add a few more of the nectarine pieces and spoon over a little of the jam mixture. Repeat the layers with the remaining ingredients, finishing with a spoonful of yogurt. Sprinkle any remaining oat cereal over the top of each sundae.

4. Decorate with the reserved nectarine pieces and serve immediately.

1

2

3

Apricot Flapjacks

Fuller for longer

Extra low sat fat

Super low calorie

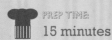 MAKES 10

 PREP TIME:
15 minutes

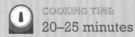 COOKING TIME:
20–25 minutes

nutritional information per bar	293 kcals, 16.5g fat, 3g sat fat, 17g total sugars, 0.4g salt, 3g fibre, 32g carbs, 3.5g protein

Just one of these tasty flapjacks gives you morning-long sustenance and is a great way to get iron and fibre.

INGREDIENTS

sunflower oil, for oiling

175 g/6 oz low-fat spread

85 g/3 oz demerara sugar

55 g/2 oz clear honey

140 g/5 oz dried apricots, chopped

2 tsp sesame seeds

225 g/8 oz porridge oats

1. Preheat the oven to 180°C/350°F/Gas Mark 4. Very lightly oil a 26 x 17-cm/10½ x 6½-inch shallow baking tin.

2. Put the spread, sugar and honey into a small saucepan over a low heat and heat until the ingredients have melted together – do not boil. When the ingredients are warm and well combined, stir in the apricots, sesame seeds and oats.

3. Spoon the mixture into the prepared tin and lightly level with the back of a spoon. Cook in the preheated oven for 20–25 minutes, or until golden brown. Remove from the oven, cut into 10 bars and leave to cool completely before removing from the baking tin. Store the flapjacks in an airtight tin and consume within 2–3 days.

FREEZING TIP
After cutting the flapjacks, pop into a freezer bag, freeze and store for up to 3 months.

Fuller for longer

Extra low sat fat

Super low calorie

Cherry & Almond Muesli

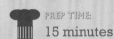 SERVES 10

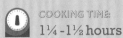 PREP TIME:
15 minutes

COOKING TIME:
1¼ - 1½ hours

nutritional information per serving	242 kcals, 11g fat, 3.5g sat fat, 14g total sugars, 0.1g salt, 5g fibre, 28g carbs, 6g protein

Lots of crunch with just a touch of sweetness, this filling cereal will keep you going until lunchtime.

INGREDIENTS

1 spray vegetable oil spray
225 g/8 oz porridge oats
50 g/1¾ oz desiccated coconut
50 g/1¾ oz flaked almonds
55 g/2 oz ground linseeds
¼ tsp salt
125 ml/4 fl oz maple syrup
4 tbsp water
1 tbsp vegetable oil
1 tsp vanilla extract
100 g/3½ oz dried cherries, chopped

1. Preheat the oven to 140°C/275°F/Gas Mark 1. Line a large baking sheet with baking paper and spray it lightly with the vegetable oil spray.

2. In a large bowl, combine the oats, coconut, almonds, linseeds and salt and stir to mix well. In a small bowl, combine the maple syrup, water, vegetable oil and vanilla extract. Pour the liquid mixture over the dry mixture and stir well. Pour the mixture on to the prepared baking sheet and spread out into an even layer.

3. Bake in the preheated oven for about 45 minutes, then stir well and spread out again into an even layer. Continue to bake for a further 30–40 minutes until crisp and beginning to colour. Stir in the cherries and leave to cool to room temperature.

4. Store in a tightly covered container at room temperature for up to a week.

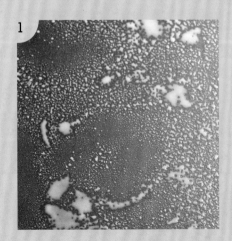

HEALTHY HINT
Replace the coconut with the same weight of pumpkin seeds, for an even healthier option.

Apricot & Apple Compote

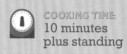 SERVES 4

PREP TIME:
5 minutes

COOKING TIME:
10 minutes
plus standing

nutritional information per serving	163 kcals, 0.4g fat, 0g sat fat, 39g total sugars, trace salt, 6g fibre, 41g carbs, 2g protein

Dried fruits are a concentrated package of vitamins, antioxidants, iron and fibre – a perfect start to the day!

INGREDIENTS

100 g/3½ oz dried apricots
85 g/3 oz dried apple
55 g/2 oz raisins
1 vanilla pod, split lengthways
300 ml/10 fl oz apple juice
low-fat soya yogurt, to serve

1. Cut any large pieces of fruit in half. Place the apricots, apples and raisins in a single layer in a frying pan and add the vanilla pod.

2. Pour over the apple juice and place the pan over a medium heat. Heat gently until almost boiling. Remove from the heat, cover, and leave to stand for about 30 minutes, or until the fruit is plump and tender.

3. Remove the vanilla pod. Serve the compote immediately, with soya yogurt spooned over the top.

FREEZING TIP
This compote
freezes well for
3 months. Place in
a freezer safe
container then seal
and freeze. Thaw
in the refrigerator
overnight.

Fuller for longer

Extra low sat fat

Cranberry & Seed Muesli

 SERVES 6

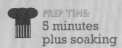 PREP TIME: 5 minutes plus soaking

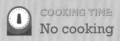 COOKING TIME: No cooking

nutritional information per serving | 330 kcals, 13g fat, 2g sat fat, 14g total sugars, trace salt, 8g fibre, 36g carbs, 9g protein

If you are bored with dry, over-sweetened muesli from a packet then try this naturally sweetened alternative.

INGREDIENTS

175 g/6 oz jumbo porridge oats

40 g/1½ oz rye flakes

40 g/1½ oz whole unblanched almonds, roughly chopped

40 g/1½ oz dried cranberries

2 tbsp sunflower seeds

2 tbsp pumpkin seeds

2 tbsp golden linseeds

2 crisp eating apples

400 ml/14 fl oz apple juice, plus extra to pour

1. Place the oats, rye flakes, almonds, cranberries, sunflower seeds, pumpkin seeds and linseeds in a large bowl and stir well.

2. Core and roughly grate the apples and stir thoroughly into the dry ingredients.

3. Stir in the apple juice, cover, and leave to soak for about an hour, or refrigerate overnight.

4. To serve, spoon the mixture into six serving bowls. Serve with a small jug of extra apple juice for pouring over the muesli.

1

2

3

BE PREPARED
Mix a larger batch of the dry ingredients and store in an airtight container for 3-4 weeks, ready to add the fresh apple and apple juice.

Pumpkin & Pecan Pancakes

Extra low sat fat

Super low calorie

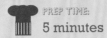 SERVES 6

 PREP TIME:
5 minutes

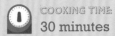 COOKING TIME:
30 minutes

nutritional information per serving	228 kcals, 4.5g fat, 0.8g sat fat, 28g total sugars, 0.6g salt, 1.6g fibre, 43.7g carbs, 6g protein

Adding nuts and nutrient-rich pumpkin to these mouth-watering pancakes gives them a real health boost.

INGREDIENTS

140 g/5 oz plain flour

20 g/¾ oz chopped pecan nuts

50 g/1¾ oz soft light brown sugar

2 tsp baking powder

½ tsp cinnamon

¼ tsp salt

1 egg

300 ml/10 fl oz semi-skimmed buttermilk

200 g/7 oz peeled and cooked pumpkin, (prepared weight), mashed

1 tsp vanilla extract

1 spray vegetable oil spray

125 ml/4 fl oz maple syrup, to serve

1. In a medium bowl, combine the flour, pecan nuts, brown sugar, baking powder, cinnamon and salt. In a large bowl, whisk the egg, buttermilk, pumpkin and vanilla extract. Whisk the dry ingredients into the wet ingredients and mix well.

2. Spray a non-stick frying pan with the vegetable oil spray and heat over a medium–high heat. When hot, ladle in the batter 50 ml/2 fl oz at a time to make 8–10-cm/3–4-inch pancakes.

3. Cook for about 2–3 minutes or until bubbles begin to burst in the top and the base is lightly coloured. Flip over and cook for about a further 2 minutes or until the second side is lightly coloured. Serve immediately with maple syrup.

1

1

3

HEALTHY HINT Use wholemeal flour to increase the fibre content.

Extra low sat fat

Super low calorie

Grape Pancake Stacks

 SERVES 4

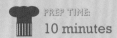 PREP TIME:
10 minutes

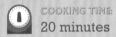 COOKING TIME:
20 minutes

nutritional information per serving	235 kcals, 5g fat, 1g sat fat, 14g total sugars, 0.5g salt, 2g fibre, 44g carbs, 6g protein

These dairy-free fruit pancakes are very easy to make and take just minutes to cook.

INGREDIENTS

150 g/5½ oz plain flour
1½ tsp baking powder
250 ml/9 fl oz white grape juice
1 large egg
175 g/6 oz red seedless grapes, halved or quartered
sunflower oil, for brushing
sprigs of grapes, to serve

1. Sift together the flour and baking powder into a large bowl. Add the grape juice and egg then whisk to a smooth, bubbly batter. Stir in the grapes.

2. Preheat a griddle or large, heavy-based frying pan over a high heat until very hot and brush lightly with oil. Reduce the heat to medium and, using a small ladle, pour three separate scoops of the batter onto the hot pan.

3. Cook for 1–2 minutes, or until just set and golden underneath. Flip over with a palette knife and cook the other side for about 1 minute, or until golden underneath. Set aside and keep warm. Repeat with the remaining batter until you have about 20 pancakes.

4. Stack the pancakes on warmed plates. Serve each stack with sprigs of grapes and serve immediately.

1

2

3
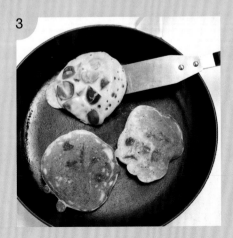

BE PREPARED
The batter can be prepared several hours in advance. Prepare to the end of step 1, cover and store in the refrigerator until ready to cook.

Fuller for longer

Wheat, gluten
& dairy free

Gluten- and Dairy-free Breakfast Cookies

 MAKES 6   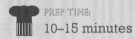 PREP TIME:
10–15 minutes   COOKING TIME:
12–15 minutes

nutritional information per cookie	318 kcals, 17g fat, 5.5g sat fat, 24g total sugars, 0.2g salt, 2.5g fibre, 40g carbs, 5.5g protein

These wheat, dairy and gluten-free cookies are great for a sustaining breakfast on the run.

INGREDIENTS

sunflower oil, for greasing
115 g/4 oz Brazil nuts
85 g/3 oz icing sugar
100 g/3½ oz buckwheat flour
½ tsp gluten-free baking powder
½ tsp xanthan gum
85 g/3 oz sultanas
25 g/1 oz desiccated coconut
2 egg whites
poppy seeds and dark muscovado sugar, to sprinkle

1. Preheat the oven to 180°C/350°F/Gas Mark 4. Lightly grease a large baking sheet.

2. Place the Brazil nuts, icing sugar and buckwheat flour in a food processor and process until finely ground. Transfer the mixture to a large bowl then stir in the baking powder and xanthan gum.

3. Stir in the sultanas, coconut and egg whites and combine thoroughly using your hands, until a soft, sticky dough forms.

4. Divide the mixture into six and roll each piece into a ball. Place on the prepared baking sheet and press each ball with your fingers to create 12-cm/4½-inch rounds. Sprinkle lightly with poppy seeds and muscovado sugar.

5. Bake in the preheated oven for 12–15 minutes, or until firm and just beginning to brown. Leave to cool on the baking sheet before serving.

2

4

4

SOMETHING DIFFERENT

For a change of flavour, replace the sultanas with an equal amount of chopped dried apricots and the Brazils with chopped blanched almonds.

Fuller for longer

Extra low sat fat

Super low calorie

Wheat, gluten
& dairy free

Millet Porridge with Apricot Purée

 SERVES 4   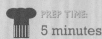 PREP TIME: 5 minutes   COOKING TIME: 25 minutes

nutritional information per serving	289 kcals, 3g fat, 1g sat fat, 12g total sugars, 0.6g salt, 2.5g fibre, 52g carbs, 4.5g protein

Gluten-free millet makes a good replacement for oats and the apricots will boost your iron intake for the day.

INGREDIENTS

225 g/8 oz millet flakes
450 ml/16 fl oz soya milk
pinch of salt
freshly grated nutmeg, to serve

apricot purée
115 g/4 oz dried apricots, roughly chopped
300 ml/10 fl oz water

1. To make the apricot purée, put the apricots into a saucepan and cover with the water. Bring to the boil, then reduce the heat and simmer, half covered, for 20 minutes until the apricots are very tender. Use a hand-held blender or transfer the apricots, along with any water left in the saucepan, to a food processor or blender and process until smooth. Set aside.

2. To make the porridge, put the millet flakes into a saucepan and add the milk and salt. Bring to the boil, then reduce the heat and simmer for 5 minutes, stirring frequently, until cooked and creamy.

3. To serve, spoon into four bowls and top with the apricot purée and a little nutmeg.

1

1

2

COOK'S NOTE Use plump, soft apricots to give a smooth purée.

Fuller for longer

Extra low sat fat

Super low calorie

Courgette Fritters

 MAKES 25

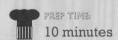 PREP TIME:
10 minutes

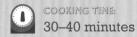 COOKING TIME:
30–40 minutes

nutritional information per fritter	28 kcals, 1g fat, 0.3g sat fat, 0.3g total sugars, trace salt, 0.3g fibre, 3g carbs, 1g protein

Quick to make, these fritters are ideal for a filling start to the day. To save time, you could prepare the batter the night before. Beat well before adding the courgettes, adding a little more milk if needed.

INGREDIENTS

100 g/3½ oz self-raising flour
2 eggs, beaten
50 ml/2 fl oz milk
300 g/10½ oz courgettes
2 tbsp fresh thyme
1 tbsp sunflower oil
salt and pepper

1. Sift the flour into a large bowl and make a well in the centre. Add the eggs to the well and, using a wooden spoon, gradually draw in the flour.

2. Slowly add the milk to the mixture, stirring constantly to form a thick batter.

3. Meanwhile, grate the courgettes over a sheet of kitchen paper placed in a bowl to absorb some of the juices.

4. Add the courgettes, thyme and salt and pepper to taste to the batter and mix thoroughly, for about a minute.

5. Heat the oil in a large, heavy-based frying pan. Taking a tablespoon of the batter for a medium-sized fritter, spoon the mixture into the hot oil and cook, in batches, for 3–4 minutes on each side.

6. Remove the fritters with a slotted spoon and drain thoroughly on absorbent kitchen paper. Keep each batch warm in the oven while making the rest. Allow five fritters per person and serve immediately.

Sausage & Potato Omelette

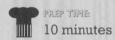 SERVES 4

 PREP TIME:
10 minutes

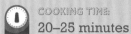 COOKING TIME:
20–25 minutes

nutritional information per serving	330 kcals, 12.5g fat, 2.5g sat fat, 7.5g total sugars, 1g salt, 6.5g fibre, 38g carbs, 16g protein

All the flavour and colour of a full cooked breakfast in one easy, healthy, low-fat, high-protein omelette - yum!

INGREDIENTS

4 wheat, gluten and dairy-free sausages (meat or vegetarian)

sunflower oil, for frying

4 boiled potatoes, cooled and diced

8 cherry tomatoes

4 eggs, beaten

salt and pepper

1. Preheat the grill to medium–high. Arrange the sausages on a foil-lined grill pan and cook under the preheated grill, turning occasionally, for 12–15 minutes, or until cooked through and golden brown. Leave to cool slightly, then slice into bite-sized pieces.

2. Meanwhile, heat a little oil in a large, heavy-based frying pan with a heatproof handle over a medium heat. Add the potatoes and cook until golden brown and crisp all over, then add the tomatoes and cook for a further 2 minutes. Arrange the sausages in the pan so that there is an even distribution of potatoes, tomatoes and sausages.

3. Add a little more oil to the pan if it seems dry. Season the beaten eggs to taste and pour the mixture over the ingredients in the pan. Cook for 3 minutes, without stirring or disturbing the eggs. Place the pan under the preheated grill for 3 minutes, or until the top is just cooked. Cut into wedges to serve.

1

2

3

SOMETHING
DIFFERENT
Try replacing
the sausage
with chopped
mushrooms or
shredded spinach.

Low on carbs

Fuller for longer

Extra low sat fat

Super low calorie

Baked Mushrooms with Herb Ricotta

 SERVES 4

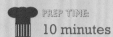 PREP TIME: 10 minutes

 COOKING TIME: 15–20 minutes

nutritional information per serving	86 kcals, 7g fat, 3g sat fat, 1g total sugars, 0.1g salt, 1.5g fibre, 1g carbs, 5g protein

Ricotta cheese is relatively low in fat in comparison with other cheeses and is a good source of protein and calcium.

INGREDIENTS

4 large flat mushrooms
1 tbsp olive oil
1 shallot, roughly chopped
25 g/1 oz fresh flat-leaf parsley
1 tbsp snipped fresh chives
140 g/5 oz ricotta cheese
salt and pepper

1. Preheat the oven to 200°C/400°F/Gas Mark 6. Remove the stalks from the mushrooms and set aside. Place the mushrooms in a shallow baking dish and brush with the oil.

2. Put the mushroom stalks, shallot, parsley and chives in a food processor and blend until finely chopped. Season to taste with salt and pepper.

3. Place the chopped ingredients in a large bowl with the ricotta and stir to mix evenly.

4. Spoon the herb ricotta onto the top of the mushrooms. Bake in the preheated oven for 15–20 minutes, or until tender and bubbling. Serve immediately.

1

2

4

GOES WELL WITH
Chunky slices of sourdough bread, either plain or toasted, make a really good accompaniment to the mushrooms and soak up the tasty juices.

Breakfast Burrito

 SERVES 1

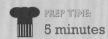 PREP TIME:
5 minutes

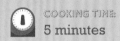 COOKING TIME:
5 minutes

nutritional information per serving	288 kcals, 6g fat, 2.5g sat fat, 4g total sugars, 2.8g salt, 6g fibre, 47g carbs, 15g protein

This breakfast has fibre, protein and carbohydrate to keep you feeling full and a hit of vitamin C, too.

INGREDIENTS

2 egg whites

pinch of salt

¼ tsp pepper

1 spring onion, thinly sliced

1 spray vegetable oil spray

30 g/1 oz red or green pepper, deseeded and diced

2 tbsp canned black beans, drained and rinsed

1 wholemeal flour tortilla, warmed

15 g/½ oz crumbled feta cheese

2 tbsp salsa

1 tsp finely chopped fresh coriander, plus extra leaves to garnish

1. In a small bowl, combine the egg whites, salt, pepper and spring onion and stir well.

2. Spray a non-stick frying pan with vegetable oil spray and place it over a medium–high heat. Add the red pepper and cook, stirring, for about 3 minutes or until it begins to soften. Reduce the heat to medium, pour in the egg mixture and cook, stirring often, for a further 1–2 minutes or until the egg sets.

3. Put the beans in a microwave-safe bowl and microwave on high for about 1 minute or until heated through.

4. Spoon the cooked egg mixture onto the tortilla. Top with the beans, cheese, salsa and coriander. Serve immediately, garnished with whole coriander leaves.

Low on carbs

Fuller for longer

Spinach Scramble with Toasted Rye Bread

 SERVES 4

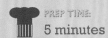 PREP TIME:
5 minutes

 COOKING TIME:
5–6 minutes

nutritional information per serving	300 kcals, 19g fat, 6g sat fat, 1.5g total sugars, 1.1g salt, 3g fibre, 13g carbs, 21g protein

Rye bread has a rich, nutty flavour and is higher in nutrients than bread made with wheat flour.

INGREDIENTS

200 g/7 oz young spinach leaves, roughly shredded

8 large eggs

3 tbsp skimmed milk

15 g/½ oz butter

4 slices rye bread

salt and pepper

freshly grated nutmeg, to serve

1. Heat a large frying pan or a wok over a high heat and add the spinach. Stir for 1–2 minutes, or until the leaves are wilted. Remove from the heat, tip into a sieve and squeeze out as much of the excess moisture as possible. Set aside and keep warm.

2. Break the eggs into a bowl, add the milk and season to taste with salt and pepper. Beat lightly with a fork until evenly mixed.

3. Melt the butter in the pan or wok over a medium heat. Add the eggs and stir until just beginning to set. Add the spinach and stir until lightly set.

4. Meanwhile, preheat a grill to medium and lightly toast the rye bread.

5. Spoon the spinach scramble over the toast, sprinkle with nutmeg and serve immediately.

1

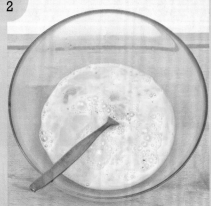

2

3

HEALTHY HINT
If you're on
a low-fat diet,
replace the butter with
your favourite low-fat
spread.

Fuller for longer

Super low calorie

Poached Eggs in Tomato Sauce

 SERVES 4    PREP TIME: 10 minutes    COOKING TIME: 30–35 minutes

nutritional information per serving	299 kcals, 16g fat, 5g sat fat, 4.5g total sugars, 1.6g salt, 4g fibre, 21g carbs, 17g protein

This rustic egg dish is perfect for brunch, but it's satisfying enough to hold its own at lunch as well.

INGREDIENTS

1 tbsp olive oil

1 small onion, diced

2 garlic cloves, finely chopped

½ tsp salt

½ tsp pepper

¼ tsp chilli flakes

4 tbsp red wine

400 g/14 oz canned chopped tomatoes, with juice

2 tsp finely chopped fresh oregano, thyme, basil, sage or other fresh herb

4 eggs

4 slices toasted wholemeal rustic bread, to serve

2 tbsp finely chopped Kalamata olives, to serve

55 g/2 oz grated Parmesan cheese, to serve

1. Heat the oil in a large frying pan over a medium–high heat. Add the onion and garlic and cook, stirring occasionally, for about 5 minutes or until soft. Add the salt, pepper, chilli flakes and wine and cook for a further few minutes until the liquid has mostly evaporated. Add the tomatoes and their juice, bring to the boil, then reduce the heat to medium–low and simmer for about 15–20 minutes or until the sauce thickens. Stir in the fresh herbs.

2. Make four wells in the sauce and carefully crack the eggs into them. Cover and simmer for about 7–9 minutes or until the whites are set but the yolks are still runny.

3. Put the toast slices on four serving plates. Carefully scoop the eggs out of the sauce and place one on each slice of toast. Place spoonfuls of the sauce around the egg and top with a sprinkling of chopped olives and Parmesan cheese. Serve immediately.

Fuller for longer

Extra low sat fat

Mushrooms on Toast

 SERVES 4

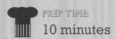 PREP TIME: 10 minutes

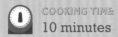 COOKING TIME: 10 minutes

nutritional information per serving	352 kcals, 11g fat, 1.5g sat fat, 3g total sugars, 1.6g salt, 5g fibre, 53g carbs, 11g protein

Wild and dark mushrooms provide the antioxidant mineral selenium, as well as other immune-boosting chemicals.

INGREDIENTS

4 large slices French-style bread, each 1 cm/ ½ inch thick, or 2 individual baguettes, cut lengthways

3 tbsp olive oil

2 garlic cloves, crushed

225 g/8 oz chestnut mushrooms, sliced

225 g/8 oz mixed wild mushrooms

2 tsp lemon juice

2 tbsp chopped fresh flat-leaf parsley

salt and pepper

1. Place the slices of bread on a ridged griddle pan and toast on both sides until golden. Reserve and keep warm.

2. Meanwhile, heat the oil in a frying pan. Add the garlic and cook gently for a few seconds, then add the chestnut mushrooms. Cook, stirring constantly, over a high heat for 3 minutes. Add the wild mushrooms and cook for a further 2 minutes. Stir in the lemon juice.

3. Season to taste with salt and pepper and stir in the chopped parsley.

4. Spoon the mushroom mixture over the top of the warm toast and serve immediately.

1

2

3

SOMETHING
DIFFERENT
Look out for packs
of mixed mushrooms
that are ideal for
this recipe.

Red Pepper Booster

Extra low sat fat

Super low calorie

Wheat, gluten & dairy free

 SERVES 2

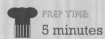 PREP TIME: 5 minutes

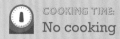 COOKING TIME: No cooking

nutritional information per serving	113 kcals, 0.9g fat, 0g sat fat, 22g total sugars, 0.9g salt, 5g fibre, 22g carbs, 4g protein

Pour yourself a glass of goodness! This is the perfect choice for a healthier drink option and will look really inviting served in a jug with ice cubes.

INGREDIENTS

250 ml/9 fl oz carrot juice

250 ml/9 fl oz tomato juice

2 large red peppers, deseeded and roughly chopped

1 tbsp lemon juice

pepper

lemon slices, to garnish

1. Pour the carrot juice and tomato juice into a food processor or blender and process gently until combined.

2. Add the red peppers and lemon juice. Season with plenty of pepper and process until smooth. Pour the mixture into glasses, garnish with lemon slices and serve.

1

2

2

Fuller for longer

Extra low sat fat

Banana Breakfast Shake

 SERVES 2 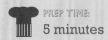 PREP TIME: 5 minutes 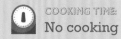 COOKING TIME: No cooking

nutritional information per serving	348 kcals, 4.5g fat, 1g sat fat, 59g total sugars, trace salt, 10g fibre, 70g carbs, 10g protein

A speedy, sustaining breakfast-in-a-glass, for days when time is short and you need long-lasting energy.

INGREDIENTS

2 large ripe bananas
2 tbsp oat bran
2 tbsp honey
1 tbsp lemon juice
300 ml/10 fl oz soya milk
ground cinnamon, to serve

1. Roughly chop the bananas and place in a large jug with the oat bran, honey and lemon juice. Add the soya milk.

2. Blend the ingredients with an electric hand-held blender, or tip into a food processor or blender and process until smooth and bubbly.

3. Pour the shake into tall glasses and sprinkle with cinnamon. Serve immediately.

1

1

2

Crunchy Brunch Wraps

 SERVES 4

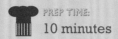 PREP TIME:
10 minutes

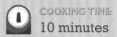 COOKING TIME:
10 minutes

nutritional information per serving	390 kcals, 21g fat, 6g sat fat, 2g total sugars, 2.3g salt, 3g fibre, 32.5g carbs, 20.5g protein

These healthy but hearty brunch wraps are easy to eat on the go and contain enough nutrition to keep you going until the afternoon.

INGREDIENTS

4 eggs
140 g/5 oz lean pancetta cubes
4 soft corn tortillas
85 g/3 oz baby spinach leaves
2 tbsp pumpkin seeds, toasted

dressing
2 tbsp fresh orange juice
2 tbsp low-fat natural yogurt
salt and pepper

1. Place the eggs in a saucepan of cold water, then place over a high heat and bring to the boil. Reduce the heat and simmer gently for 10 minutes. Drain the eggs, crack the shells and place under cold running water for 2 minutes. Peel off the shells and cut the eggs into quarters.

2. Meanwhile, place a heavy-based frying pan over a medium–high heat. Fry the pancetta cubes, stirring occasionally, for about 5 minutes, or until golden brown and the fat runs out. Remove the cubes with a slotted spoon and drain well on absorbent kitchen paper.

3. Place the four corn tortillas on a work surface and divide the spinach leaves between them. Top with the egg quarters and scatter with pancetta and pumpkin seeds.

4. To make the dressing, stir together the orange juice and yogurt in a small bowl and season to taste with salt and pepper. Drizzle the dressing over the ingredients in the tortillas and fold up the wraps. Serve immediately.

Fuller for longer

Extra low sat fat

Super low calorie

Wholemeal Muffins

 MAKES 10

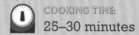 PREP TIME:
15 minutes

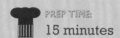 COOKING TIME:
25–30 minutes

nutritional information
per muffin

173 kcals, 4.5g fat, 0.7g sat fat, 9.5g total sugars, 0.5g salt,
2g fibre, 27g carbs, 4.5g protein

*A sweet, flavour-packed treat with none of the guilt.
This muffin is crammed with healthy ingredients!*

INGREDIENTS

225 g/8 oz self-raising
wholemeal flour

2 tsp baking powder

25 g/1 oz light muscovado sugar

100 g/3½ oz dried apricots, finely
chopped

1 banana, mashed with
1 tbsp orange juice

1 tsp orange rind,
finely grated

300 ml/10 fl oz skimmed milk

1 egg, beaten

3 tbsp corn oil

2 tbsp porridge oats

fruit spread, honey or maple
syrup, to serve

1. Preheat the oven to 200°C/400°F/Gas Mark 6. Place 10 paper muffin cases in a muffin tin. Sift the flour and baking powder into a mixing bowl, adding any husks that remain in the sieve. Stir in the sugar and chopped apricots.

2. Make a well in the centre of the dry ingredients and add the banana, orange rind, milk, beaten egg and oil. Mix together well to form a thick batter. Divide the batter evenly among the 10 paper cases.

3. Sprinkle each muffin with a few porridge oats and bake in the preheated oven for 25–30 minutes, or until well risen and firm to the touch. Transfer the muffins to a wire rack to cool slightly. Serve the muffins warm with a little fruit spread, honey or maple syrup.

Fuller for longer

Extra low sat fat

Super low calorie

Wheat, gluten
& dairy free

Raw Buckwheat & Almond Porridge

 SERVES 6

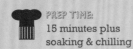 PREP TIME:
15 minutes plus
soaking & chilling

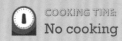 COOKING TIME:
No cooking

nutritional information per serving	288 kcals, 8g fat, 1g sat fat, 0.7g total sugars, trace salt, 6g fibre, 45g carbs, 5.5g protein

Packed with magnesium for your heart, this is also rich in delicious nutty buckwheat, an ideal grain substitute.

INGREDIENTS

almond milk
70 g/2½ oz whole raw almonds, soaked overnight in water
300 ml/10 fl oz water

porridge
350 g/12 oz raw buckwheat groats, soaked in cold water for 90 minutes
1 tsp cinnamon
2 tbsp light agave nectar, plus extra to serve
sliced strawberries, to serve

1. To make the almond milk, drain the almonds and transfer to a blender or food processor. Blend the almonds with the water. Keep the blender running for a minute or two to break down the almonds as much as possible.

2. Pour the mixture into a sieve lined with muslin and squeeze through as much of the liquid as possible into a large bowl or jug. You should get approximately 300 ml/10 fl oz of raw almond milk.

3. Rinse the soaked buckwheat thoroughly in cold water. Transfer to the blender or food processor with the almond milk, cinnamon and agave nectar. Blend to a slightly coarse texture.

4. Chill the mixture for at least 30 minutes or overnight. It can be stored, covered, in the refrigerator for 3 days.

5. Serve in small bowls, topped with strawberries and agave nectar to taste.

Light Lunches

Minestrone Soup

Fuller for longer

Extra low sat fat

Super low calorie

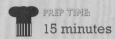 SERVES 4

 PREP TIME:
15 minutes

 COOKING TIME:
30–35 minutes

nutritional information per serving	99 kcals, 1g fat, 0.2g sat fat, 9g total sugars, 1.2g salt, 5g fibre, 19g carbs, 6g protein

This more-ish Italian soup is bursting with carotenes which fight cancer and heart disease.

INGREDIENTS

2 sprays olive oil

1 onion, finely chopped

1 large carrot, about 115 g/4 oz, diced

2 celery sticks, sliced

1 bouquet garni

400 g/14 oz canned chopped tomatoes

55 g/2 oz dried soup pasta or spaghetti broken into short lengths

850 ml/1½ pints vegetable stock

½ small cabbage, about 225 g/8 oz

pepper

1. Heat the oil in a large saucepan, add the onion, carrot and celery and sauté gently for 5 minutes, stirring frequently. Add the bouquet garni with the chopped tomatoes. Half-fill the empty tomato can with water, swirl to remove all the remaining tomatoes then pour into the pan.

2. Add the pasta with the stock and bring to the boil. Reduce the heat to a simmer and cook for 12 minutes, or until the vegetables are almost tender.

3. Discard any outer leaves and hard central core from the cabbage and shred. Wash well, then add to the saucepan with pepper to taste. Continue to cook for 5–8 minutes, or until all the vegetables are tender, but still firm to the bite. Discard the bouquet garni and serve divided equally between four warmed bowls.

1

2

3

Mediterranean Fish Soup

Low on carbs

Protein packed

Fuller for longer

Extra low sat fat

Super low calorie

 SERVES 4

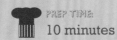 PREP TIME:
10 minutes

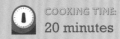 COOKING TIME:
20 minutes

nutritional information per serving	233 kcals, 5g fat, 0.8g sat fat, 5g total sugars, 1.2g salt, 1.5g fibre, 6g carbs, 40g protein

Packed with protein to keep hunger pangs away, this is also rich in immune-boosting zinc and plant compounds.

INGREDIENTS

1 tbsp olive oil
1 large onion, chopped
2 garlic cloves, finely chopped
425 ml/15 fl oz fish stock
150 ml/5 fl oz dry white wine
1 bay leaf
1 sprig each fresh thyme, rosemary and oregano
450 g/1 lb firm white fish fillets (such as cod, monkfish or halibut), skinned and cut into 2.5-cm/1-inch cubes
450 g/1 lb fresh mussels, prepared
400 g/14 oz canned chopped tomatoes
225 g/8 oz cooked, peeled prawns
salt and pepper
fresh thyme sprigs, to garnish
French bread, to serve

1. Heat the olive oil in a large saucepan and gently fry the onion and garlic for 2–3 minutes, or until just softened.

2. Pour in the stock and wine and bring to the boil. Tie the bay leaf and herbs together with clean string and add to the saucepan together with the fish and mussels. Stir well, cover and simmer for 5 minutes.

3. Stir in the tomatoes and prawns and continue to cook for a further 3–4 minutes, or until piping hot and the fish is cooked through.

4. Discard the herbs and any mussels that have not opened. Season to taste, then ladle into warmed bowls. Garnish with sprigs of fresh thyme and serve with French bread.

1

2

3

Extra low sat fat

Super low calorie

Carrot & Cumin Soup

 SERVES 2

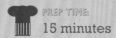 PREP TIME:
15 minutes

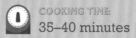 COOKING TIME:
35–40 minutes

nutritional information per serving	135 kcals, 1g fat, 0.1g sat fat, 15g total sugars, 0.1g salt, 7g fibre, 15g carbs, 3g protein

A high-fibre soup ideal for slimmers, this is also rich in vitamin A, essential for healthy skin.

INGREDIENTS

1 carrot, finely chopped

1 garlic clove, chopped

1 shallot, finely chopped

1 ripe tomato, skinned and chopped

½ tsp ground cumin

200 ml/7 fl oz vegetable stock

1 bouquet garni

2 tsp dry sherry (optional)

pepper

pinch of cumin and 1 tbsp half-fat crème fraîche (optional), to garnish

1. Place the carrot, garlic, shallot, tomato, cumin, stock and bouquet garni in a lidded saucepan.

2. Bring to simmering point over a high heat, then reduce the heat and simmer for 30 minutes, or until the vegetables are tender. Cool slightly and remove the bouquet garni.

3. Pour the soup into a food processor or blender and purée until smooth.

4. Return to the saucepan, add the sherry, if using, and reheat. Season to taste with pepper. Remove from the heat and ladle into warmed mugs or bowls. Garnish with cumin and a swirl of crème fraîche, if using, and serve.

1

2

3

GOES WELL WITH
A slice of wholegrain
bread will provide
additional calories
and B vitamins.

Fuller for longer

Extra low sat fat

Super low calorie

Roast Tomato Soup

 SERVES 4

 PREP TIME:
25 minutes

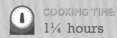 COOKING TIME:
1¼ hours

nutritional information per serving	263 cals, 15g fat, 3.5g sat fat, 12g total sugars, 2g salt, 7g fibre, 26g carbs, 9g protein

This soup is a source of sulphides from the onion and garlic, both of which are natural antibiotics.

INGREDIENTS

1.3 kg/3 lb plum tomatoes, halved, stalk ends removed
1 red onion, roughly chopped
6 garlic cloves, peeled
2 tbsp olive oil
¾ tsp salt
1 tsp pepper
6 sprigs fresh thyme, plus extra to garnish
1 litre/1¾ pints vegetable stock
2 tbsp lemon juice

parmesan croûtons
100 g/3½ oz cubed wholemeal bread
2 tbsp olive oil
½ tsp salt
¼ tsp pepper
2 tbsp Parmesan cheese

1. Preheat the oven to 230°C/450°F/Gas Mark 8. On a large baking sheet, toss the tomatoes, onion and garlic with the olive oil, salt, pepper and thyme. Spread the vegetables out into a single layer, arranging the tomatoes cut-side up, and roast in the preheated oven for about 45 minutes or until the vegetables are soft.

2. To make the croûtons, reduce the oven heat to 150°C/300°F/Gas Mark 2. Toss the cubed bread with the olive oil and sprinkle with the salt and pepper. Spread the bread cubes in an even layer on a baking sheet and bake in the preheated oven for about 25 minutes. Sprinkle with the cheese, return to the oven and bake for a further 5 minutes or until the cheese is melted and beginning to brown.

3. Finish the soup while the croûtons are baking. Purée the vegetables along with the stock, in several batches, in a blender or food processor. Alternatively purée the vegetables and stock in a large saucepan using a hand-held blender.

4. Bring the purée to the boil in a large saucepan over a high heat. Reduce the heat to medium and simmer, stirring occasionally, for about 15 minutes. Just before serving, stir in the lemon juice. Serve in warmed bowls, garnished with croûtons and thyme sprigs.

Fuller for longer

Extra low sat fat

Super low calorie

Wheat, gluten & dairy free

Shaker Salad in a Jar

 SERVES 4

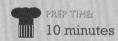 PREP TIME:
10 minutes

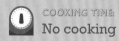 COOKING TIME:
No cooking

nutritional information **per serving**   144 kcals, 9g fat, 1g sat fat, 13g total sugars, trace salt, 4g fibre, 15g carbs, 2g protein

Sprouting seeds and pulses boost the nutritional content of this salad and it is terrific to take to work or school.

INGREDIENTS

2 crisp red eating apples
lime juice, for sprinkling
1 large carrot
6-cm/2½-inch piece cucumber
85 g/3 oz mung bean sprouts
55 g/2 oz sunflower seed sprouts
40 g/1½ oz alfalfa seed sprouts

dressing
1 tbsp lime juice
3 tbsp olive oil
1 tsp grated fresh ginger
1 tsp light muscovado sugar
salt and pepper, to taste

1. Core, quarter and roughly grate the apples into a bowl, then sprinkle with lime juice to prevent browning. Roughly grate the carrot and the cucumber into two separate bowls.

2. To make the dressing, place all of the dressing ingredients in a large jar or sealable food container, large enough to hold the salad with room to spare. Shake well to mix. Alternatively, make individual salads in four small jars.

3. Add all the bean and seed sprouts to the jar, then layer the apple, carrot and cucumber into the jar. Replace the lid until required.

4. To serve, shake the jar to coat the ingredients in the dressing, then either eat straight from the jar or transfer to bowls to serve.

1

2

3

COOK'S NOTE
To sprout the seeds,
soak overnight in a jar
of cold water, drain,
then rinse and drain
twice a day for
3-5 days until
sprouted.

Fuller for longer

Extra low sat fat

Super low calorie

Mixed Green Salad with Yogurt Dressing

 SERVES 4

 PREP TIME:
15 minutes

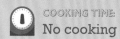 COOKING TIME:
No cooking

nutritional information per serving	109 kcals, 7g fat, 1.5g sat fat, 8.5g total sugars, 0.2g salt, 2.5g fibre, 8.5g carbs, 3g protein

Just what the doctor ordered to boost your vitamin C intake, this salad is zinging with fresh flavours.

INGREDIENTS

85 g/3 oz cucumber, sliced

6 spring onions, chopped

2 tomatoes, sliced

1 yellow pepper, deseeded and cut into strips

2 celery sticks, cut into strips

4 radishes, sliced

85 g/3 oz rocket

1 tbsp chopped fresh mint, to garnish (optional)

dressing

2 tbsp lemon juice

1 garlic clove, crushed

150 g/5½ oz low-fat natural yogurt

2 tbsp olive oil

salt and pepper

1. To make the salad, gently mix the cucumber, spring onions, tomatoes, yellow pepper strips, celery, radishes and rocket in a large serving bowl.

2. To make the dressing, stir the lemon juice, garlic, natural yogurt and olive oil together in a small bowl until thoroughly combined. Season with salt and pepper to taste.

3. Spoon the dressing over the salad and toss to mix. Garnish the salad with chopped mint (if using) and serve.

1

2

3

Fuller for longer

Super low calorie

Lentil & Goat's Cheese Tomatoes

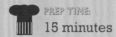 SERVES 4

 PREP TIME: 15 minutes

COOKING TIME: 35–45 minutes

nutritional information per serving	182 kcals, 10g fat, 5g sat fat, 7g total sugars, 0.5g salt, 4.5g fibre, 13.5g carbs, 10g protein

Lentils are a good source of protein and soluble fibre, which helps lower blood cholesterol.

INGREDIENTS

55 g/2 oz dried Puy lentils

4 beef tomatoes

1 tbsp olive oil

2 large shallots, finely chopped

1 garlic clove, crushed

1 tbsp chopped fresh thyme

100 g/3½ oz hard goat's cheese, diced

salt and pepper

mixed salad, to serve

1. Bring a small saucepan of water to the boil over a medium–high heat. Add the lentils, return to the boil and cook for 20–25 minutes, or until tender. Drain well.

2. Meanwhile, preheat the oven to 200°C/400°F/Gas Mark 6. Cut a slice from the tops of the tomatoes and set aside. Scoop out the pulp from the centre and chop roughly.

3. Heat the oil in a frying pan over a medium heat and fry the shallots, stirring, for 3–4 minutes to soften. Add the garlic and chopped tomato pulp and cook for a further 3–4 minutes, or until any excess moisture has evaporated.

4. Place the tomatoes in a shallow baking dish. Stir the lentils and thyme into the frying pan, and season to taste with salt and pepper. Stir in the goat's cheese and then spoon the mixture into the tomatoes.

5. Replace the lids on the tomatoes and bake in the preheated oven for 15–20 minutes, or until tender. Serve immediately, with mixed salad.

2

3

4

GOES WELL WITH
A crisp green
salad of
shredded lettuce
leaves and sliced
cucumber makes
a refreshing
accompaniment to
the tomatoes.

Protein packed

Fuller for longer

Extra low sat fat

Chicken Noodle Bowl

 SERVES 4   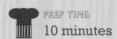 PREP TIME: 10 minutes   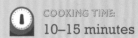 COOKING TIME: 10–15 minutes

nutritional information per serving : 382 kcals, 7g fat, 2g sat fat, 4g total sugars, 1.4g salt, 4g fibre, 41g carbs, 44g protein

This quick and easy, low-fat lunch dish is a great standby when time is tight.

INGREDIENTS

600 ml/1 pint reduced-salt chicken stock

1 small green chilli, deseeded and chopped

1 garlic clove, finely chopped

500 g/1 lb 2 oz chicken breasts, cut into strips

1 tsp Thai fish sauce

1 bunch spring onions, chopped

200 g/7 oz dried medium egg noodles

200 g/7 oz fresh beansprouts

salt and pepper

1. Put the chicken stock into a large saucepan over a medium–high heat and add the chilli and garlic. Bring to the boil.

2. Stir in the strips of chicken and bring back to the boil, then reduce the heat slightly and simmer for 5 minutes. Add the fish sauce and spring onions.

3. Add the egg noodles and simmer for about 4 minutes, stirring occasionally, or until the noodles are just tender.

4. Stir in the beansprouts and heat for about a minute, then season to taste with salt and pepper. Serve immediately in bowls.

Warm Shredded Beef Tabbouleh Salad

 SERVES 4

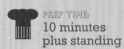 PREP TIME:
10 minutes
plus standing

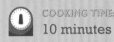 COOKING TIME:
10 minutes

nutritional information per serving	329 kcals, 13g fat, 3.5g sat fat, 4g total sugars, 0.2g salt, 4.5g fibre, 26g carbs, 27g protein

A special salad for a summer lunch party or simply for a tasty treat when you need one!

INGREDIENTS

100 g/3½ oz bulgar wheat

400 g/14 oz lean beef fillet

200 g/7 oz fresh flat-leaf parsley, finely chopped

140 g/5 oz fresh mint, finely chopped

1 red onion, thinly sliced

2 tomatoes, diced

1 tbsp extra virgin olive oil, plus extra for brushing

juice of 2 lemons

salt and pepper

1. Place the bulgar wheat in a bowl and pour over boiling water to cover. Leave to soak for 10 minutes. Drain thoroughly, pressing out any excess moisture.

2. Meanwhile, place a griddle pan or frying pan over a high heat. Season the beef fillet with salt and pepper, brush lightly with oil and cook for 2–3 minutes on each side, turning once. Remove from the heat and cover with foil for 5 minutes.

3. Mix together the parsley, mint, onion, tomatoes and bulgar wheat in a bowl. Stir in the olive oil and lemon juice and season to taste with salt and pepper.

4. Slice the beef fillet into 2.5-cm/1-inch thin strips. Serve the bulgar wheat salad on warmed plates and arrange the beef slices on top, then pour over the meat juices.

1

2

3

Low on carbs

Protein packed

Fuller for longer

Extra low sat fat

Super low calorie

Tuna Sashimi

 SERVES 4

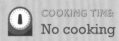 PREP TIME:
10–15 minutes

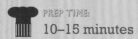 COOKING TIME:
No cooking

nutritional information **per serving** — 150 kcals, 5g fat, 1g sat fat, 5g total sugars, 1.5g salt, 2g fibre, 7g carbs, 19g protein

You should choose only the freshest tuna for this light, refreshing raw food, sashimi-style salad.

INGREDIENTS

2 carrots, roughly grated

1 celery stick, thinly sliced

1 small red onion, thinly sliced

2.5-cm/1-inch piece ginger, grated

300 g/10½ oz fresh tuna fillet

1 tsp sesame seeds, to serve

dressing

3 tbsp rice vinegar or white wine vinegar

1 tbsp lemon juice

2 tbsp shoyu or soy sauce

1 tsp sesame oil

1. To make the dressing, place the vinegar, lemon juice, shoyu and sesame oil in a jar and shake well to mix.

2. Place the carrot, celery, onion and ginger in a bowl and stir to mix. Pour over half of the dressing and toss to coat evenly.

3. Arrange the salad on four serving plates. Using a very sharp knife, slice the tuna thinly and arrange the slices over the salad.

4. Spoon over the remaining dressing and serve sprinkled with sesame seeds.

1

2

3

SOMETHING
DIFFERENT
For a hotter
flavour, omit the
ginger and add
½ teaspoon of
wasabi paste to
the dressing.

Fuller for longer

Extra low sat fat

Red Pepper Hummus, Rocket & Artichoke Wraps

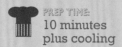 SERVES 4

 PREP TIME:
10 minutes
plus cooling

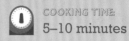 COOKING TIME:
5–10 minutes

nutritional information per serving	350 kcals, 13g fat, 1.5g sat fat, 5g total sugars, 1.6g salt, 11g fibre, 50g carbs, 12g protein

A variation on classic hummus using roasted sweet peppers, which add a rich, sweet flavour and extra nutrients.

INGREDIENTS

hummus
1 large red pepper, quartered and deseeded
400 g/14 oz canned chickpeas, drained and rinsed
2 tbsp lemon juice
2 tbsp tahini
salt and pepper

4 wholemeal tortillas
40 g/1½ oz rocket leaves
200 g/7 oz artichoke hearts in oil, drained and quartered

1. Preheat a grill to high. Place the pepper quarters, cut-side down, on a grill pan and grill until the skins are blackened and charred. Put the peppers in a polythene bag, seal and leave to cool.

2. To make the hummus, remove the skins from the peppers and place in a food processor with the chickpeas, lemon juice and tahini. Process until almost smooth. Season to taste with salt and pepper.

3. Divide the hummus between the tortillas, placing the hummus down the centre of the wrap. Top with the rocket leaves and artichoke hearts.

4. Fold the tortilla sides over to enclose the filling and serve immediately.

1

2

3

SOMETHING DIFFERENT
For a fuller flavour, add ½ teaspoon of crushed dried chillies and a crushed garlic clove to the hummus before processing.

Low on carbs

Fuller for longer

Super low calorie

Smoked Mackerel Salad

 SERVES 5

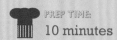 PREP TIME: 10 minutes

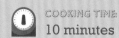 COOKING TIME: 10 minutes

nutritional information per serving	331 kcals, 26g fat, 5.5g sat fat, 5.2g total sugars, 1.5g salt, 2.4g fibre, 5.5g carbs, 19g protein

A good salad for picnics, as the chunky pieces pack easily and keep their texture well.

INGREDIENTS

4 eggs

175 g/6 oz broccoli, cut into small florets

300 g/10½ oz smoked mackerel fillet, skinned

1 crisp, sweet eating apple, such as Gala

dressing

juice of 1 lemon, plus extra for sprinkling

2 tbsp extra light mayonnaise

1 tsp Dijon mustard

2 tbsp snipped fresh chives

salt and pepper

1. Place the eggs in a saucepan of cold water. Bring the pan to the boil over a high heat and boil for 10 minutes. Drain the eggs, crack the shells and rinse in cold water. Peel and cut into slices.

2. Meanwhile, bring a saucepan of water to the boil over a high heat. Place the broccoli in the pan and boil for 3–4 minutes. Drain and rinse in cold water.

3. Slice the mackerel diagonally into strips. Core and slice the apple, sprinkling with a little lemon juice.

4. To make the dressing, place the lemon juice, mayonnaise, mustard and chives in a jar and shake well to mix evenly. Season to taste with salt and pepper.

5. Combine the eggs, broccoli, mackerel and apple in a salad bowl and pour in the dressing, tossing with two forks to mix thoroughly. Serve immediately.

1

3

5

GOES WELL WITH
Fresh, crusty slices
of multigrain bread
make a good partner
for this salad.

Fuller for longer

Extra low sat fat

Wholewheat Spaghetti with Edamame Beans

 SERVES 4

 PREP TIME:
5 minutes

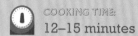 COOKING TIME:
12–15 minutes

nutritional information per serving	410 kcals, 11g fat, 1g sat fat, 3g total sugars, 0.3g salt, 12g fibre, 64g carbs, 18g protein

Edamame beans are packed with high quality protein, fibre and vitamins, which can help to reduce cholesterol.

INGREDIENTS

350 g/12 oz wholewheat spaghetti

200 g/7 oz frozen edamame (soya) beans

2 tbsp extra virgin olive oil

2 garlic cloves, thinly sliced

finely grated rind of 1 lemon

salt and pepper

1. Bring a saucepan of lightly salted water to the boil over a high heat. Add the spaghetti, return to the boil and cook for 10–12 minutes, or until tender but still firm to the bite. Add the edamame beans to the pan for the final 3 minutes. Drain the spaghetti and beans well and keep warm in the pan.

2. Meanwhile, place the oil in a small frying pan over a low heat and stir in the garlic. Reduce to a very low heat to infuse for about 10 minutes, stirring occasionally, without allowing the garlic to sizzle or brown.

3. Add the lemon rind, garlic and oil to the spaghetti and beans and toss to combine evenly. Season to taste with salt and pepper and serve immediately.

1

2

3

SOMETHING
DIFFERENT
Meat eaters may also
like to add some thin
strips of lean, cooked
ham or prosciutto at
step 3 with the
lemon rind.

Crab Salad Sandwiches

Fuller for longer

Extra low sat fat

Super low calorie

 SERVES 4

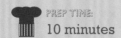 PREP TIME:
10 minutes

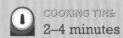 COOKING TIME:
2–4 minutes

nutritional information per serving	300 kcals, 10g fat, 1g sat fat, 3g total sugars, 2.3g salt, 6g fibre, 30.5g carbs, 27g protein

This high-taste sandwich is packed with B vitamins to help keep your nervous system healthy.

INGREDIENTS

1 small fennel bulb with leaves

400 g/14 oz crabmeat, picked over

2 tbsp light mayonnaise

2 celery sticks, finely chopped

2 spring onions, thinly sliced

1 tbsp lemon juice

½ tsp salt

8 slices wholemeal bread

1. Remove the leaves from the fennel bulb, then chop and reserve 1 teaspoon of the leaves. Slice the bulb in half lengthways, then carefully cut each half into paper-thin slices and set aside.

2. In a small bowl, combine the crabmeat, mayonnaise, celery, spring onions, fennel leaves, lemon juice and salt. Stir to mix well.

3. Toast the bread. Divide the crab mixture evenly between four slices of the toasted bread. Top with the paper-thin fennel slices and the remaining four slices of bread. Cut each sandwich in half diagonally and serve immediately.

1

2

3

HEALTHY HINT
To reduce the fat content
down even lower, try
using fat-free Greek
yogurt instead of the
mayonnaise.

Fuller for longer

Extra low sat fat

Super low calorie

Falafel Pitta Pockets

 SERVES 4

 PREP TIME: 15 minutes

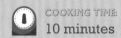 COOKING TIME: 10 minutes

nutritional information per serving	221 kcals, 5g fat, 1g sat fat, 5g total sugars, 2g salt, 6g fibre, 35g carbs, 7.6g protein

This gorgeous filled pitta contains a variety of nutrients and the chickpeas are high in vitamin E and fibre.

INGREDIENTS

2 garlic cloves

2 tbsp each of chopped fresh flat-leaf parsley and coriander

1 tsp ground cumin

½ tsp salt

275 g/9¾ oz canned chickpeas, drained and rinsed

2 spring onions, sliced

2 tbsp plain flour

1 tsp baking powder

1 tbsp vegetable oil

tzatziki sauce

280 g/10 oz cucumber, peeled, deseeded and grated

½ tsp salt

125 g/4½ oz low-fat natural yogurt

2 tbsp lemon juice

2 tbsp chopped fresh mint leaves

to serve

2 wholemeal pittas, halved and warmed

2 tomatoes, diced

100 g/3½ oz lettuce, shredded

1. To make the falafel patties, chop the garlic in a food processor. Add the parsley, coriander, cumin and salt and process until the herbs are finely chopped. Add the chickpeas, spring onions, flour and baking powder and process until the texture resembles coarse breadcrumbs. Form the falafel mixture into eight patties, about 5 mm/¼-inch thick.

2. To make the sauce, put the grated cucumber on a double layer of kitchen paper and sprinkle with half the salt. Set aside. In a medium bowl, combine the yogurt, the remaining salt, lemon juice and mint and stir to combine. Bundle the cucumber up in the kitchen paper and, holding over the sink, squeeze out the excess juice. Mix the cucumber into the yogurt mixture. Chill until ready to serve.

3. In a heavy-based frying pan, heat the oil over a medium–high heat. When the oil is hot, add the patties and cook for about 3 minutes or until browned on the base. Turn over and cook until browned on the other side. Drain on kitchen paper.

4. To serve, stuff two falafel patties into each pitta half, drizzle with some of the sauce, then add diced tomato and shredded lettuce. Serve immediately.

Polenta Bruschettas with Tapenade

 SERVES 4

 PREP TIME:
20 minutes
plus setting

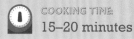 COOKING TIME:
15–20 minutes

nutritional information per serving	280 kcals, 20g fat, 3g sat fat, 1.5g total sugars, 0.9g salt, 2g fibre, 19g carbs, 3g protein

Polenta makes a change from bread in this flavourful Italian lunch and olive oil is one of the healthiest oils.

INGREDIENTS

500 ml/18 fl oz boiling water

100 g/3½ oz quick-cook polenta

2 tbsp olive oil, plus extra for brushing

16 cherry vine tomatoes

salt and pepper

tapenade

25 g/1 oz sun-dried tomatoes

55 g/2 oz pitted black olives

2 tbsp salted capers, rinsed

2 tbsp chopped fresh flat-leaf parsley

1 garlic clove, crushed

juice of ½ lemon

2 tbsp extra virgin olive oil

1. Brush a 450 g/1 lb loaf tin with oil. Place the water in a large pan with a pinch of salt and bring to the boil.

2. Sprinkle in the polenta and stir constantly over moderate heat for about 5 minutes, until thick and smooth. Remove from the heat, stir in the oil and salt and pepper to taste, then spread into the prepared tin. Leave to set.

3. To make the tapenade, finely chop the sun-dried tomatoes, olives, capers and parsley. Mix with the garlic, lemon juice and oil, and season to taste.

4. Preheat the grill to high. Cut the polenta into eight slices and arrange on a baking sheet with the cherry vine tomatoes. Brush the polenta with oil and grill until golden, turning once.

5. Serve the polenta slices topped with a spoonful of tapenade and the grilled tomatoes.

SOMETHING
DIFFERENT
Try swapping the tomatoes
with vitamin C-rich grilled
red pepper quarters.

Brown Rice Lunchbowl

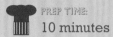 SERVES 4

 PREP TIME:
10 minutes

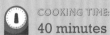 COOKING TIME:
40 minutes

nutritional information per serving	468 kcals, 20g fat, 4.5g sat fat, 2.5g total sugars, 0.5g salt, 4g fibre, 63g carbs, 9g protein

The unbeatable flavour and texture of fresh green asparagus is perfect for this salad.

INGREDIENTS

300 g/10½ oz brown basmati rice

1 bay leaf

600 ml/1 pint gluten-free vegetable stock or water

250 g/9 oz asparagus, cut into 3-cm/1¼-inch chunks

juice of 1 lime

2 tbsp extra virgin olive oil

70 g/2½ oz Brazil nuts, roughly chopped

salt and pepper

1. Place the rice and bay leaf in a large saucepan with the stock over a high heat and bring to the boil. Stir lightly then reduce the heat. Cover and simmer for about 35 minutes, stirring occasionally to prevent sticking, until all the liquid is absorbed and the rice is just tender. Remove and discard the bay leaf.

2. Meanwhile, bring a saucepan of water to the boil over a high heat. Add the asparagus and boil for 3–5 minutes, or until just tender. Alternatively, steam the asparagus for 5–6 minutes over the boiling water to preserve more nutrients. Drain well.

3. Combine the rice and asparagus in a large bowl and pour over the lime juice and olive oil. Mix well to combine thoroughly.

4. Stir in the Brazil nuts and season to taste with salt and pepper. Serve warm or cold.

1

2

3

COOK'S NOTE
Asparagus is very
perishable but will store
for 2-3 days with
the cut ends in damp
kitchen paper, inside
a polythene bag in
the refrigerator.

Fuller for longer

Extra low sat fat

Spicy Jacket Potatoes

 SERVES 4

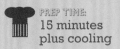 PREP TIME:
15 minutes
plus cooling

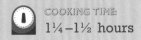 COOKING TIME:
1¼–1½ hours

nutritional information per serving	373 kcals, 5.5g fat, 0.5g sat fat, 8g total sugars, 0.13g salt, 10g fibre, 70g carbs, 14g protein

Adding spices to your meals not only increases flavour - the antioxidant content also gets a boost.

INGREDIENTS

4 baking potatoes, each about 300 g/10½ oz

1 tbsp vegetable oil (optional)

400 g/14 oz canned chickpeas, drained and rinsed

1 tsp ground coriander

1 tsp ground cumin

4 tbsp chopped fresh coriander

150 g/5½ oz low-fat natural yogurt

salt and pepper

salad leaves, to serve

1. Preheat the oven to 200°C/400°F/Gas Mark 6. Scrub the potatoes and pat them dry with absorbent kitchen paper. Prick the potatoes all over with a fork, brush with oil (if using) and season to taste with salt and pepper. Place the potatoes on a baking sheet in the preheated oven and bake for 1–1¼ hours, or until cooked through. Cool for 10 minutes.

2. Meanwhile, place the chickpeas in a large mixing bowl and mash with a fork or potato masher. Stir in the ground coriander, cumin and half the chopped fresh coriander. Cover the bowl with clingfilm and set aside.

3. Halve the cooked potatoes and scoop the flesh into a bowl, keeping the shells intact. Mash the flesh until smooth and gently mix into the chickpea mixture with the yogurt. Season with salt and pepper to taste. Place the potato shells on a baking sheet and fill with the potato and chickpea mixture. Return the potatoes to the oven and bake for 10–15 minutes until heated through.

4. Garnish the potatoes with the remaining chopped coriander and serve with salad leaves.

1

2

3

Protein packed

Fuller for longer

Extra low sat fat

Super low calorie

Chicken Tacos

 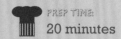 SERVES 4

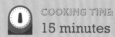 PREP TIME:
20 minutes

COOKING TIME:
15 minutes

nutritional information
per serving

300 kcals, 2g fat, 0.5g sat fat, 7.5g total sugars, 1.6g salt, 4g fibre, 43.5g carbs, 29g protein

Salsa is a brilliant way of adding fibre and vitamin C to these more-ish tacos and is virtually fat free.

INGREDIENTS

salsa
½ red onion, diced

2 jalapeño peppers, deseeded and diced

4 tomatoes, diced

2 tbsp chopped fresh coriander

3 tbsp lime juice

½ tsp salt

chicken filling
2 tsp soft light brown sugar

2 tsp ground cumin

1 tsp chilli powder

½ tsp salt

½ tsp pepper

400 g/14 oz skinless, boneless chicken breasts

8 small corn tortillas (25 g/1 oz each), to serve

200 g/7 oz lettuce, shredded, to serve

1. Make the salsa by putting the onion, jalapeño peppers and tomatoes into a medium bowl and stirring well. Add the coriander, lime juice and salt and stir to combine.

2. To make the chicken filling, preheat the grill to high or put a griddle pan over a high heat. In a small bowl, combine the brown sugar, cumin, chilli powder, salt and pepper. Rub the spice mixture all over the chicken breasts. Grill the chicken breasts over high heat for about 4 minutes per side or until lightly browned on the outside and cooked through with no signs of pink when cut through with a sharp knife. Remove from heat and leave for about 5 minutes, then slice into 5-mm/¼-inch thick slices.

3. To serve, heat the tortillas briefly on the grill, then top with the chicken, salsa and lettuce. Serve immediately.

Fuller for longer

Extra low sat fat

Super low calorie

Turkey, Mozzarella & Pepper Panini

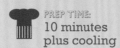 SERVES 4

 PREP TIME:
10 minutes
plus cooling

 COOKING TIME:
10 minutes

nutritional information per serving	281 kcals, 6g fat, 3g sat fat, 10g total sugars, 1g salt, 3.5g fibre, 35g carbs, 23g protein

Rich Mediterranean flavours combine in these irresistible toasted sandwiches, which are surprisingly low in fat.

INGREDIENTS

2 red peppers, halved and deseeded

4 ciabatta rolls

200 g/7 oz roast turkey breast, sliced

125 g/4½ oz half-fat mozzarella, sliced

handful of basil leaves

2 tbsp sweet chilli sauce

1. Preheat a grill to hot. Place the peppers cut-side down on a grill pan and cook under the preheated grill for 4–6 minutes, or until the skins are blackened and charred. Put the peppers in a polythene bag, seal and leave to cool. Remove the skins once cool.

2. Split the rolls open and arrange the turkey on the bottom halves. Top with the mozzarella and basil leaves. Drizzle with chilli sauce.

3. Slice the peppers thickly, then arrange over the other ingredients in the rolls.

4. Place a griddle pan over a high heat and cook the paninis, pressing lightly with a fish slice, or place under a hot grill, until golden. Serve immediately.

1

2

3

SOMETHING
DIFFERENT
The paninis
can be served
untoasted, as
crusty sandwich
rolls - the filling
will be just as
tasty!

Extra low sat fat

Super low calorie

Squash & Couscous Salad

 SERVES 4

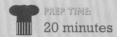 PREP TIME:
20 minutes

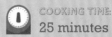 COOKING TIME:
25 minutes

nutritional information per serving	200 kcals, 8.5g fat, 1.1g sat fat, 7g total sugars, 0.14g salt, 3g fibre, 27g carbs, 4g protein

Baking the squash brings out its sweetness in this tasty recipe, which is packed with health-promoting carotenes.

INGREDIENTS

500 g/1 lb 2 oz butternut squash, deseeded, peeled and cut into small chunks

1 onion, roughly chopped

1 garlic clove, crushed (optional)

2 tbsp olive oil

125 g/4½ oz couscous

4 sun-dried tomatoes in oil, drained and chopped

200 ml/7 fl oz boiling water

3 tbsp chopped fresh flat-leaf parsley

1 tbsp lemon juice

salt and pepper

1. Preheat the oven to 200°C/400°F/Gas Mark 6. Place the squash, onion, garlic (if using) and oil in a roasting tin. Toss together. Cover the tin tightly with foil and bake in the preheated oven for 20–25 minutes, or until the vegetables are just tender. Leave to stand for 5 minutes before removing the foil.

2. While the vegetables are cooking, place the couscous and sun-dried tomatoes in a heatproof bowl. Pour over the boiling water, then cover the bowl and leave to stand for 10 minutes, or until all the liquid is absorbed.

3. Fluff up the couscous with a fork. Add the couscous mixture to the vegetables and their juices in the roasting tin with the parsley and lemon juice. Season to taste with salt and pepper, then gently toss together. Serve warm or cold.

1

2

3

HEALTHY HINT
For a gluten-free version, use brown rice rather than couscous – it will also then contain more fibre and B vitamins.

Extra low sat fat

Super low calorie

Prawn Rice Noodle Salad

 SERVES 4

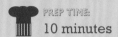 PREP TIME: 10 minutes

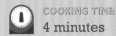 COOKING TIME: 4 minutes

nutritional information per serving	260 kcals, 6g fat, 1g sat fat, 3g total sugars, 1g salt, 0.3g fibre, 39g carbs, 10g protein

This refreshing salad is good for a light summer lunch, especially for picnics and lunchboxes.

INGREDIENTS

175 g/6 oz vermicelli rice noodles

200 g/7 oz cooked, peeled prawns

½ cucumber, cut into matchsticks

1 shallot, very thinly sliced

2 tbsp finely chopped fresh coriander

dressing
2 tbsp groundnut oil

juice of 1 lime

1 tbsp sweet chilli sauce

1 tsp Thai fish sauce

1 tsp freshly grated ginger

1. Place the noodles in a bowl, cover with boiling water and leave to stand for 4 minutes, or until tender but firm to the bite. Drain, rinse in cold water and drain again thoroughly.

2. To make the dressing, place all of the ingredients in a small jug and beat lightly with a fork to mix.

3. Place the prawns, cucumber, shallot and coriander in a large bowl and stir in the noodles. Pour in the dressing and toss thoroughly with two forks to mix evenly. Serve immediately.

1

2

3

BE PREPARED
This salad will
store well for up
to 24 hours in the
refrigerator if you
cover the bowl
with clingfilm.

Protein packed

Fuller for longer

Extra low sat fat

Super low calorie

Thai Crab Cakes

 SERVES 6

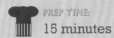 PREP TIME:
15 minutes

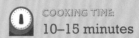 COOKING TIME:
10–15 minutes

nutritional information per serving	114 kcals, 4g fat, 0.7g sat fat, 4g total sugars, 0.6g salt, 1g fibre, 8g carbs, 11g protein

This is an ideal lunch for slimmers, as the protein and fibre content will keep you full for hours.

INGREDIENTS

300 g/10½ oz canned crabmeat, drained

1–2 fresh bird's eye chillies, deseeded and finely chopped

6 spring onions, thinly sliced

140 g/5 oz courgettes, grated

115 g/4 oz carrot, grated

1 tbsp chopped fresh coriander

2 tbsp cornflour

2 egg whites

1 spray sunflower oil

lime wedges, to serve

spicy dipping sauce

150 g/5½ oz low-fat natural yogurt

hot pepper sauce, to taste

2 tsp sesame seeds

1. Place the crabmeat in a bowl and stir in the chillies, spring onions, courgette, carrot and coriander. Add the cornflour and mix well.

2. Beat the egg whites together in a separate bowl then pour into the crab mixture and mix together.

3. Heat a large frying pan and lightly spray with the oil, then drop small spoonfuls of the crab mixture into the pan. Fry the crab cakes over a low heat for 3–4 minutes, pressing down with the back of a spatula. Turn over halfway through cooking. Cook the crab cakes in batches.

4. To make the sauce, mix the yogurt and hot pepper sauce in a small bowl and stir in the sesame seeds. Spoon into a small bowl and use as a dipping sauce for the cooked crab cakes. Serve immediately, with lime wedges alongside for squeezing over.

Fuller for longer

Super low calorie

Stuffed Aubergines

 SERVES 4    PREP TIME: 15 minutes   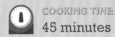 COOKING TIME: 45 minutes

nutritional information per serving	287 kcals, 14g fat, 4.2g sat fat, 9g total sugars, 2.1g salt, 9g fibre, 29g carbs, 12.5g protein

Rich-tasting and satisfying, it's hard to believe these aubergines can easily form part of a low-calorie diet.

INGREDIENTS

2 medium aubergines
(1.25 kg/2 lb 12 oz)

1 tbsp olive oil

1 small onion, diced

2 garlic cloves, finely chopped

140 g/5 oz quinoa

350 ml/12 fl oz vegetable stock

1 tsp salt

pinch of pepper

2 tbsp flaked almonds, toasted

2 tbsp finely chopped fresh mint,
plus extra sprigs to garnish

85 g/3 oz feta cheese,
crumbled

1. Preheat the oven to 230°C/450°F/Gas Mark 8. Place the aubergines on a baking sheet and bake for 15 minutes or until soft. Remove from the oven and leave to cool slightly.

2. Meanwhile, heat the olive oil in a large, heavy-based frying pan over a medium–high heat. Add the onion and garlic and cook, stirring occasionally, for about 5 minutes or until soft. Add the quinoa, stock, salt and pepper.

3. Cut each aubergine in half lengthways and scoop out the flesh, leaving a 5-mm/¼-inch thick border inside the skin so they hold their shape. Chop the flesh and stir it into the quinoa mixture in the frying pan. Reduce the heat to medium–low, cover and cook for about 15 minutes or until the quinoa is cooked through. Remove from the heat and stir in the almonds, chopped mint and half of the cheese.

4. Divide the quinoa mixture equally among the aubergine skins and top with the remaining cheese. Bake in the oven for about 10–15 minutes or until the cheese is bubbling and beginning to brown. Garnish with the mint sprigs and serve.

Chicken & Sun-dried Tomato Pasta *118*

Moroccan-style Turkey *120*

Roast Pork with Gingered Apples *122*

Jerk Chicken *124*

Beef Stir-fry *126*

Pork Meatballs with Tomato Sauce *128*

Chicken & Vegetable Enchiladas *130*

Lean Beef Burgers *132*

Chicken Chilli *134*

Spanish Rice with Pork & Peppers *136*

Turkey & Cranberry Burgers *138*

Braised Soy & Ginger Pork Fillets *140*

Spicy Chicken Skewers *142*

Garlic Chicken with Leeks *144*

Turkey & Oat Meatballs *146*

Prawns with Ginger *148*

Thai Fish Curry *150*

Grilled Salmon with Mango & Lime Salsa *152*

Fish Tacos with Avocado Salsa *154*

Halibut with Romesco Sauce *156*

Chipotle-lime Prawn Burgers *158*

Chunky Monkfish Hotpot *160*

Rustic Fish Casserole *162*

Prawn & Sausage Jambalaya *164*

Meat & Fish Mains

Extra low sat fat

Super low calorie

Chicken & Sun-dried Tomato Pasta

 SERVES 6 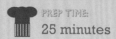 PREP TIME: 25 minutes 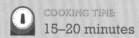 COOKING TIME: 15–20 minutes

nutritional information per serving	297 kcals, 4g fat, 0.6g sat fat, 1g total sugars, 1.7g salt, 2g fibre, 48.2g carbs, 20g protein

The full flavour of this antioxidant-rich pasta dish belies its tiny fat and saintly low saturates content.

INGREDIENTS

115 g/4 oz sun-dried tomatoes (not packed in oil)

350 g/12 oz skinless, boneless chicken breasts, diced

1 tsp salt

½ tsp pepper

1 spray vegetable oil spray

2 garlic cloves

40 g/1½ oz fresh basil, plus leaves to garnish

1 tbsp olive oil

300 g/10½ oz dried pasta

1. Put the tomatoes in a small bowl and cover with boiling water. Leave to soak for about 20 minutes until soft, then drain, discarding the soaking liquid.

2. Season the chicken with ½ teaspoon of the salt and the pepper. Coat a large, non-stick frying pan with the vegetable oil spray and heat over a medium–high heat. Add the chicken and cook, stirring occasionally, for about 5 minutes or until it is cooked through and just beginning to colour. Set aside.

3. Place the rehydrated tomatoes in a food processor along with the garlic and basil and process to a paste. Add the oil and the remaining salt and continue to process until smooth.

4. Cook the pasta according to the instructions on the packet. Just before draining, scoop out and reserve about 125 ml/4 fl oz of the cooking water. Drain the pasta.

5. Toss the hot pasta with the sun-dried tomato pesto, chicken and as much of the pasta cooking water as needed to make a sauce to coat the pasta. Garnish with basil leaves and serve immediately.

Moroccan-style Turkey

Protein packed

Fuller for longer

Extra low sat fat

Super low calorie

 SERVES 4

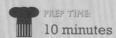 PREP TIME:
10 minutes

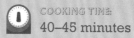 COOKING TIME:
40–45 minutes

nutritional information per serving	254 kcals, 2.5g fat, 0.5g sat fat, 7g total sugars, 0.8g salt, 4g fibre, 22g carbs, 28g protein

The chickpeas and apricots in this spiced casserole mean that it is high in iron for healthy blood.

INGREDIENTS

400 g/14 oz skinless, boneless turkey breasts, diced

1 onion, sliced

1 tsp ground cumin

½ tsp ground cinnamon

1 tsp hot chilli sauce

240 g/8½ oz canned chickpeas, drained and rinsed

600 ml/1 pint chicken stock

12 dried apricots

40 g/1½ oz cornflour

75 ml/2½ fl oz cold water

2 tbsp chopped fresh coriander

cooked couscous, rice or jacket sweet potatoes, to serve

1. Put the turkey, onion, cumin, cinnamon, chilli sauce, chickpeas and stock into a large saucepan or frying pan and bring to the boil. Reduce the heat, cover and simmer for 15 minutes.

2. Stir in the apricots and return to the boil. Reduce the heat, cover and simmer for a further 15 minutes, or until the turkey is thoroughly cooked and tender.

3. Blend the cornflour with the water in a small bowl and stir into the casserole. Return to the boil, stirring constantly, and cook until the casserole thickens. Reduce the heat, cover and simmer for a further 5 minutes.

4. Stir half of the coriander into the casserole. Transfer to a warmed serving dish and sprinkle over the remaining coriander. Serve immediately with cooked couscous, rice or jacket sweet potatoes.

FREEZING TIP
Leave to cool at
the end of Step
3, then place in
a container and
freeze for up to
1 month.

Fuller for longer

Extra low sat fat

Super low calorie

Wheat, gluten
& dairy free

Roast Pork with Gingered Apples

 SERVES 4

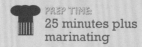 PREP TIME:
25 minutes plus marinating

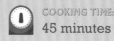 COOKING TIME:
45 minutes

nutritional information per serving	220 kcals, 4.5g fat, 1.5g sat fat, 27g total sugars, 0.8g salt, 4g fibre, 25g carbs, 20g protein

Apples make a brilliant, low-calorie change from potatoes in this unusual roast pork recipe.

INGREDIENTS

2 garlic cloves
4 tbsp red wine
2 tbsp soft brown sugar
1 tbsp gluten-free tamari (soy sauce)
1 tsp sesame oil
½ tsp ground cinnamon
¼ tsp ground cloves
1 star anise pod, broken into pieces
½ tsp pepper
350 g/12 oz pork fillet
steamed green beans, to serve

gingered apples
4 Bramley apples, chopped
1 tbsp rice vinegar
1 tbsp soft brown sugar
4 tbsp apple juice
1 tbsp fresh ginger, finely chopped

1. In a bowl large enough to hold the pork, combine the garlic, wine, brown sugar, tamari, sesame oil, cinnamon, cloves, star anise and pepper. Add the pork and toss to coat. Cover and refrigerate for at least 2 hours or overnight.

2. Preheat the oven to 190°C/375°F/Gas Mark 5. Heat a non-stick frying pan over a high heat. Remove the pork from the marinade, letting any excess run off into the bowl. Sear the pork, turning occasionally, in the hot frying pan for about 8 minutes or until browned on all sides.

3. Place the meat in an ovenproof dish and drizzle with a few spoonfuls of the marinade. Roast in the preheated oven for 15 minutes. Turn the meat over, drizzle with more of the marinade and continue to roast for about a further 30 minutes or until cooked through (insert a skewer into the centre of the meat and check that there is no pink meat).

4. While the meat is roasting, make the gingered apples. In a saucepan, combine the apples, vinegar, sugar, apple juice and ginger. Cook over a medium–high heat, stirring occasionally, until the liquid begins to boil. Reduce the heat to medium–low and simmer, stirring occasionally, for about 20 minutes or until the apples are soft and the liquid is mostly evaporated.

5. Once the pork has cooked, remove it from the oven and cover the baking dish in a 'tent' of foil. Leave the meat to rest for about 5 minutes. Slice the meat into 5-mm/¼-inch thick slices and serve with a spoonful of the gingered apples alongside and the green beans.

1

2

4

Jerk Chicken

Protein packed

Fuller for longer

Extra low sat fat

Super low calorie

 SERVES 4

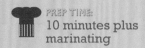 PREP TIME: 10 minutes plus marinating

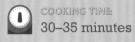 COOKING TIME: 30–35 minutes

nutritional information per serving	173 kcals, 1.5g fat, 0.5g sat fat, 3g total sugars, 2.2g salt, 0.5g fibre, 3g carbs, 37g protein

Packed with appetite-satisfying chicken and heart-friendly spices, you'll want to cook this again and again.

INGREDIENTS

4 lean chicken portions

1 bunch spring onions, roughly chopped

1–2 Scotch bonnet chillies, deseeded

1 garlic clove

5-cm/2-inch piece fresh ginger, roughly chopped

½ tsp dried thyme

½ tsp paprika

¼ tsp ground allspice

pinch ground cinnamon

pinch ground cloves

4 tbsp white wine vinegar

3 tbsp light soy sauce

pepper

salad leaves and crusty bread, to serve

1. Rinse the chicken portions and pat them dry on absorbent kitchen paper. Place them in a shallow dish and make slashes across the tops with a sharp knife.

2. Place the spring onions, chillies, garlic, ginger, thyme, paprika, allspice, cinnamon, cloves, wine vinegar, soy sauce and pepper to taste in a food processor and process until smooth.

3. Pour the spicy mixture over the chicken. Turn the chicken portions over so that they are well coated in the marinade.

4. Transfer the chicken portions to the refrigerator and leave to marinate for up to 24 hours.

5. Preheat the grill to medium. Remove the chicken from the marinade and grill for about 30–35 minutes, turning the chicken over and basting occasionally with any remaining marinade. Grill until the chicken is cooked through, so that when a sharp knife is inserted into the thickest part of the meat, the juices run clear with no traces of pink. Transfer the chicken portions to individual serving plates and serve immediately with salad leaves and crusty bread.

Low on carbs

Protein packed

Extra low sat fat

Super low calorie

Beef Stir-fry

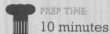 SERVES 4

 PREP TIME:
10 minutes

COOKING TIME:
10–12 minutes

nutritional information per serving	80 kcals, 1.5g fat, 0.5g sat fat, 4g total sugars, 0.4g salt, 2.5g fibre, 4.5g carbs, 10g protein

Lean beef is extremely high in iron and vegetables are all rich in vitamin C, which helps you absorb that iron.

INGREDIENTS

2–3 sprays olive oil

140 g/5 oz beef steak, such as topside (fat removed), cut into thin strips

1 orange pepper, deseeded and cut into thin strips

4 spring onions, chopped

1–2 fresh jalapeño peppers, deseeded and chopped

2–3 garlic cloves, chopped

115 g/4 oz mangetout, trimmed and cut in half diagonally

115 g/4 oz large field mushrooms, sliced

1–2 tsp hoisin sauce, or to taste

1 tbsp orange juice

85 g/3 oz rocket or watercress

1. Preheat a wok then spray in the oil and heat for 30 seconds. Add the beef and stir-fry for 1 minute or until browned. Using a slotted spoon, remove and reserve.

2. Add the orange pepper, spring onions, jalapeño peppers and garlic and stir-fry for 2 minutes. Add the mangetout and mushrooms and stir-fry for a further 2 minutes.

3. Return the beef to the wok and add the hoisin sauce and orange juice. Stir-fry for 2–3 minutes, or until the beef is tender and the vegetables are tender but still firm to the bite. Stir in the rocket and stir-fry until it starts to wilt. Serve immediately.

1

2

3

GOES WELL WITH *Serve with brown rice or wholewheat noodles to boost fibre.*

Fuller for longer

Extra low sat fat

Pork Meatballs with Tomato Sauce

 SERVES 4 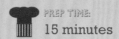 PREP TIME: 15 minutes  COOKING TIME: 40–45 minutes

nutritional information per serving	463 kcals, 10g fat, 1.5g sat fat, 10g total sugars, 0.6g salt, 6g fibre, 58g carbs, 40g protein

Lean pork is much lower in fat than many people think and is high in various minerals and B vitamins.

INGREDIENTS

400 g/14 oz lean pork fillet

4 reduced-fat pork sausages, skins removed and roughly chopped

3–4 tsp rapeseed or sunflower oil

1 onion, finely chopped

800 g/1 lb 12 oz canned chopped tomatoes

150 ml/5 fl oz chicken or vegetable stock

1 carrot, finely chopped

1 celery stick, finely chopped

1 tsp dried oregano

250 g/9 oz dried spaghetti

salt and pepper

1. Place the pork fillet in a food processor and process until finely chopped. Transfer to a bowl. Add the sausage meat and mix well, then roll into 20 walnut-sized balls.

2. Heat 2 teaspoons of oil in a large saucepan. Add the onion, cover and cook over a low heat for 2–3 minutes, or until softened. Stir in the tomatoes, stock, carrot, celery and oregano. Simmer uncovered for 15–20 minutes, or until the sauce has reduced and thickened slightly.

3. Meanwhile, heat 1 teaspoon of oil in a large frying pan. Add the meatballs in batches and fry for 2–3 minutes, adding a little extra oil if necessary and turning several times, until well browned all over. Transfer to a plate with a slotted spoon.

4. Season the sauce to taste with salt and pepper. Add the meatballs, then cover the pan and simmer for 8–10 minutes, or until cooked through. Cook the spaghetti in a large saucepan of boiling, lightly salted water for the time stated on the packet, or until tender but still firm to the bite. Drain and return to the hot pan. Add the meatballs and sauce and toss well to mix. Serve immediately.

Chicken & Vegetable Enchiladas

 SERVES 4

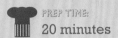 PREP TIME:
20 minutes

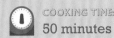 COOKING TIME:
50 minutes

nutritional information per serving	296 kcals, 7.5g fat, 3g sat fat, 5g total sugars, 2g salt, 4g fibre, 35g carbs, 25g protein

These enchiladas are packed with the plant compound lycopene, which protects against cancer and heart disease.

INGREDIENTS

2 sprays olive oil spray

2 courgettes, diced

1 red pepper, deseeded and diced

1 tsp salt

1 onion, diced

2 garlic cloves, finely chopped

1 tbsp chilli powder

1 tbsp dried oregano

175 ml/6 fl oz passata

240 ml/8¾ fl oz vegetable stock

175 g/6 oz cooked chicken breast, shredded

8 small corn tortillas (25 g/1 oz each)

75 g/2¾ oz reduced-fat Cheddar cheese, grated

1. Preheat the oven to 230°C/450°F/Gas Mark 8. Spray a large, rimmed baking tray with a spray of olive oil spray.

2. Spread the courgettes and pepper on the prepared baking tray, turning to coat in the oil. Sprinkle with half of the salt. Bake in the preheated oven for about 20 minutes or until soft and beginning to brown.

3. Meanwhile, spray a large frying pan with 1 spray of olive oil and place over a medium–high heat. Add the onion and garlic and cook, stirring, for about 5 minutes or until soft. Add the chilli powder and oregano and cook for a further minute. Add the passata and stock and bring to the boil. Reduce the heat to medium and simmer, stirring occasionally, for 5 minutes. Stir in the remaining salt. Purée the sauce, in batches, in a blender or food processor, or use a hand-held blender.

4. When the vegetables are done, remove them from the oven and reduce the heat to 180°C/350°F/Gas Mark 4. In a large bowl, combine the vegetables, shredded chicken and several spoonfuls of the sauce. Stir well.

5. Coat the base of a 23 x 33-cm/9 x 13-inch baking dish with a thin layer of the sauce. Place four of the tortillas on the base of the dish, overlapping as little as possible. Top the tortillas with the chicken-vegetable mixture and then a second layer of four tortillas. Top the stacks with the remaining sauce, then sprinkle the cheese over the top.

6. Bake in the preheated oven for about 30 minutes until the enchiladas are heated through and the cheese is bubbling and beginning to colour. Serve immediately.

Lean Beef Burgers

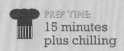 SERVES 4

 PREP TIME:
15 minutes
plus chilling

COOKING TIME:
25–30 minutes

nutritional information per serving	116 kcals, 5g fat, 2g sat fat, 6g total sugars, 0.2g salt, 2.5g fibre, 7g carbs, 11g protein

Everyone loves a tasty beef burger and, cooked our way, it really is good for you!

INGREDIENTS

175 g/6 oz fresh lean beef, such as topside, minced

2 shallots, finely chopped

1 tbsp Worcestershire sauce, or to taste

2 sprays sunflower oil spray

2 onions, thinly sliced

4 beef tomatoes

1–2 garlic cloves

pepper

tomato ketchup, to serve (optional)

mixed salad leaves, to serve

1. Put the beef mince in a bowl and add the shallots, Worcestershire sauce and pepper to taste. Mix together and, with damp hands, shape into four equal-sized burgers. Place the burgers on a plate, cover lightly with clingfilm and chill in the refrigerator until required.

2. Heat a large frying pan, spray with the oil and add the sliced onions. Cook over a low heat for 12–15 minutes, stirring frequently until the onions are tender. Keep warm if necessary. Preheat the grill to high and line the grill rack with foil.

3. Cut the tomatoes into thick slices and the garlic cloves into slivers. Stud the tomatoes with the garlic and place on the grill rack together with the burgers.

4. Cook the burgers for 3–4 minutes on each side, or according to personal preference. If the tomatoes are cooking too quickly, either remove them and add a little later or remove and keep warm. Serve each burger between the thick tomato slices with the onion garnish, ketchup, if using, and salad leaves.

Chicken Chilli

Low on carbs

Protein packed

Fuller for longer

Extra low sat fat

Super low calorie

Wheat, gluten
& dairy free

 SERVES 6

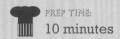 PREP TIME:
10 minutes

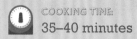 COOKING TIME:
35–40 minutes

nutritional information per serving	219 kcals, 5.5g fat, 1g sat fat, 4g total sugars, 1.1g salt, 4g fibre, 10g carbs, 26g protein

The protein-rich cannellini beans mean you have no need to add rice or potatoes to this chilli.

INGREDIENTS

1 tbsp vegetable oil

1 onion, diced

2 garlic cloves, finely chopped

1 green pepper, deseeded and diced

1 small jalapeño pepper, deseeded and diced

2 tsp chilli powder

2 tsp dried oregano

1 tsp ground cumin

1 tsp salt

500 g/1 lb 2 oz canned cannellini beans, drained and rinsed

700 ml/1¼ pints gluten-free chicken stock

450 g/1 lb cooked chicken breasts, shredded

juice of 1 lime

25 g/1 oz chopped coriander, plus leaves to garnish

1. Heat the oil in a large, heavy-based saucepan over a medium–high heat. Add the onion, garlic, pepper and jalapeño and cook, stirring occasionally, for about 5 minutes or until soft. Add the chilli powder, oregano, cumin and salt and cook, stirring, for about a further 30 seconds.

2. Add the beans and stock and bring to the boil. Reduce the heat to medium–low and simmer gently, uncovered, for about 20 minutes.

3. Ladle about half of the bean mixture into a blender or food processor and purée. Return the purée to the pan along with the shredded chicken. Simmer for about 10 minutes or until heated through. Just before serving, stir in the lime juice and coriander. Garnish with coriander leaves and serve immediately.

Spanish Rice with Pork & Peppers

 SERVES 1   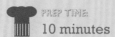 PREP TIME: 10 minutes    COOKING TIME: 45–55 minutes

nutritional information **per serving** | 476 kcals, 7g fat, 2g sat fat, 19g total sugars, 0.9g salt, 8g fibre, 65g carbs, 25g protein

A colourful taste of Spain but with a healthy twist!
The brown rice boosts the fibre and vitamin B content.

INGREDIENTS

½ tsp olive oil

75 g/2¾ oz lean pork tenderloin, cut into small cubes

1 small onion, or 2 shallots, finely chopped

1 garlic clove, chopped

1 red or orange pepper, deseeded and chopped into 1-cm/½-inch cubes

200 g/7 oz canned chopped tomatoes

1 tbsp chopped fresh parsley

pinch of saffron strands

60 g/2¼ oz, dry weight, brown basmati rice

225 ml/8 fl oz chicken or vegetable stock

pepper

1. Heat the oil in a large, heavy-based, lidded saucepan and brown the pork on all sides on a high heat. Remove with a slotted spoon and keep warm.

2. Reduce the heat to medium–high and add the onion, garlic and pepper, and stir-fry for a few minutes until everything is soft and turning golden.

3. Return the meat to the pan and add the tomatoes, parsley, saffron, rice and stock, and season to taste with pepper. Stir well to combine and to break up the tomatoes a little, and bring to a simmer. Turn the heat down to low and put the lid on.

4. Simmer for 30–40 minutes, or until the rice is tender and all the stock is absorbed. (If the rice is not cooked but the dish looks dry, add a little more hot water.) Remove from the heat and serve.

1

2

3

SOMETHING DIFFERENT
Chicken thigh fillets, skinned, make a great subsitute for the pork and are similarly rich in B vitamins and minerals.

Protein packed

Fuller for longer

Extra low sat fat

Super low calorie

Turkey & Cranberry Burgers

 SERVES 4

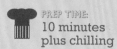 PREP TIME:
10 minutes
plus chilling

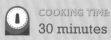 COOKING TIME:
30 minutes

nutritional information per serving	247 kcals, 3.5g fat, 0.6g sat fat, 8g total sugars, 0.7g salt, 2g fibre, 24g carbs, 29g protein

The perfect healthy way to use up leftover turkey, our supper is also simple to make and delicious too!

INGREDIENTS

350 g/12 oz lean turkey mince
1 onion, finely chopped
1 tbsp chopped fresh sage
6 tbsp dry white breadcrumbs
4 tbsp cranberry sauce
1 egg white, lightly beaten
2 tsp sunflower oil, for brushing
salt and pepper

to serve
4 toasted granary or wholemeal burger buns
½ lettuce, shredded
4 tomatoes, sliced
4 tsp cranberry sauce

1. Mix together the turkey, onion, sage, seasoning, breadcrumbs and cranberry sauce in a large bowl, then bind with egg white.

2. Press into four 10-cm/4-inch rounds, about 2 cm/¾ inch thick. Chill the burgers for 30 minutes.

3. Preheat the grill to medium and line the grill rack with baking paper, making sure the ends are secured underneath the rack to ensure they don't catch fire. Place the burgers on top and brush lightly with oil. Put under the preheated grill and cook for 10 minutes. Turn the burgers over and brush again with oil. Cook for a further 12–15 minutes, or until cooked through.

4. Fill the burger buns with lettuce, tomato and a burger, and top with cranberry sauce.

1

2

4

HEALTHY HINT
For an even
lower-calorie meal,
serve the burger
on half a bun,
as an open
sandwich.

Low on carbs

Protein packed

Fuller for longer

Extra low sat fat

Super low calorie

Braised Soy & Ginger Pork Fillets

 SERVES 4   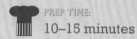 PREP TIME: 10–15 minutes   COOKING TIME: 40 minutes

nutritional information **per serving**	220 kcals, 7.5g fat, 2g sat fat, 6g total sugars, 1g salt, 3g fibre, 6g carbs, 31g protein

A Chinese-style dish that uses a low-fat cut of pork in a richly flavoured sauce.

INGREDIENTS

2 tsp sunflower oil

500 g/1 lb 2 oz lean pork fillet

4 shallots, thinly sliced

2 tsp soy sauce

1 garlic clove, crushed

1 tbsp honey

2.5-cm/1-inch piece grated fresh ginger

150 ml/5 fl oz chicken stock

250 g/9 oz closed-cup mushrooms, sliced

250 g/9 oz pak choi, quartered

salt and pepper

1. Place a wide, heavy-based frying pan or flameproof casserole dish over a high heat. Meanwhile, brush the oil over the surface of the pork.

2. Place the pork in the hot pan and fry, turning occasionally, for about 10 minutes, or until golden brown on all sides. Add the shallots to the pan and fry for 1 minute, stirring continuously.

3. Mix together the soy sauce, garlic, honey and ginger in a small bowl. Spread the soy mixture evenly over the pork in the pan.

4. Pour the stock into the pan and bring to the boil. Reduce the heat to low and simmer gently for about 20 minutes, turning the pork occasionally in the juices. Remove the pork from the pan with a slotted spoon and leave to rest on a warmed dish. Check that the pork is cooked through, with no traces of pink, and that the juices run clear when you cut into the meat.

5. Add the mushrooms and pak choi to the pan and increase the heat until boiling. Reduce the heat and simmer for 4–5 minutes, or until tender. Season to taste with salt and pepper. Slice the pork diagonally, adding the juices back to the pan.

6. Serve the sliced pork on top of the vegetables, with the juices spooned over.

2

3

5

Spicy Chicken Skewers

Protein packed

Fuller for longer

Extra low sat fat

Super low calorie

 SERVES 4

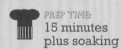 PREP TIME:
15 minutes
plus soaking

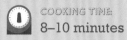 COOKING TIME:
8–10 minutes

nutritional information **per serving**

186 kcals, 2g fat, 0.5g sat fat, 12g total sugars, 0.5g salt, 1g fibre, 12g carbs, 31g protein

A simple, quick and easy supper that is ideal for slimmers watching their calories or fat intake.

INGREDIENTS

500 g/1 lb 2 oz skinless, boneless chicken breasts

3 tbsp tomato purée

2 tbsp clear honey

2 tbsp Worcestershire sauce

1 tbsp chopped fresh rosemary

250 g/9 oz cherry tomatoes

fresh rosemary sprigs, to garnish

freshly cooked couscous or rice, to serve

1. Using a sharp knife, cut the chicken into 2.5-cm/1-inch chunks and place in a bowl. Mix the tomato purée, honey, Worcestershire sauce and rosemary together in a separate bowl, then add to the chicken, stirring to coat evenly.

2. Soak eight wooden skewers in a bowl of cold water for 30 minutes to prevent them burning during cooking. Preheat the grill to hot. Thread the chicken pieces and cherry tomatoes alternately on to the skewers and place them on a grill rack.

3. Spoon over any remaining glaze and cook under the preheated hot grill for 8–10 minutes, turning occasionally, until the chicken is cooked through. Transfer to four large serving plates, garnish with a few sprigs of fresh rosemary and serve with freshly cooked couscous or rice.

1

2

3

HEALTHY HINT
To keep the calorie content low, serve just 2 tbsp couscous and add a large green leaf salad.

Low on carbs

Protein packed

Fuller for longer

Extra low sat fat

Super low calorie

Garlic Chicken with Leeks

 SERVES 4   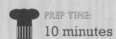 PREP TIME: 10 minutes   COOKING TIME: 8–10 minutes

nutritional information per serving	206 kcals, 5g fat, 1g sat fat, 9.5g total sugars, 1.5g salt, 2.5g fibre, 9.5g carbs, 28.5g protein

Chicken and leeks always taste great together and combine well with the unmistakable flavour of fresh ginger and soy sauce.

INGREDIENTS

450 g/1 lb skinless, boneless chicken breasts, finely chopped
1 tbsp groundnut oil
6 garlic cloves, thinly sliced
2.5-cm/1-inch piece finely grated fresh ginger
200 g/7 oz leeks, thinly sliced
4 spring onions, chopped
1 tbsp clear honey

marinade
2 tbsp rice wine
2 tbsp dark soy sauce
1 tsp sesame oil

1. To make the marinade, place the rice wine, soy sauce and sesame oil in a large mixing bowl. Add the chicken pieces and mix together.

2. Drain the chicken, reserving the marinade. Preheat a wok or large frying pan over a high heat. Add the oil and heat until very hot. Add the drained chicken and stir-fry for 3 minutes to seal.

3. Add the garlic, ginger, leeks and spring onions to the wok and fry for a further 3 minutes to soften. Add the reserved marinade and honey and stir-fry for a further minute, until the chicken is cooked through.

4. Transfer to warmed serving bowls and serve immediately.

1

2

3

GOES WELL WITH
Serve with cooked rice or noodles that can be softened by submerging in boiling water.

Turkey & Oat Meatballs

Protein packed

Fuller for longer

Extra low sat fat

Super low calorie

 SERVES 4

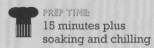 PREP TIME:
15 minutes plus
soaking and chilling

 COOKING TIME:
10–12 minutes

nutritional information per serving	191 kcals, 4g fat, 1g sat fat, 4.5g total sugars, 0.2g salt, 2.5g fibre, 15g carbs, 23g protein

Light and simple meat skewers are winners for summer barbecues, especially when served with a colourful salad.

INGREDIENTS

250 g/9 oz turkey mince
70 g/2½ oz porridge oats
4 spring onions, finely chopped
1½ tbsp chopped fresh thyme
1 egg white
olive oil, for brushing
salt and pepper
paprika, to sprinkle
mixed salad, to serve

sauce
150 g/5½ oz low-fat natural yogurt
1 garlic clove, crushed
¼ cucumber, roughly grated

1. Presoak eight bamboo skewers in cold water for about 20 minutes.

2. Place the turkey, oats, spring onions, thyme and egg white in a bowl and season to taste with salt and pepper. Mix with your hands until evenly combined. Divide the mixture into eight even-sized pieces and shape into ovals around the prepared skewers. Leave to chill in the refrigerator for an hour.

3. Preheat a grill or barbecue to high. Brush the meatballs lightly with oil and place under the hot grill, turning occasionally, for 10–12 minutes, or until golden brown and thoroughly cooked.

4. Meanwhile, make the sauce. Mix together the yogurt, garlic and cucumber in a small bowl. Sprinkle the meatball skewers with paprika and serve hot, with the sauce and a mixed salad on the side.

2

2

4

FREEZING TIP
Prepare up to
the end of step
2 then freeze
until firm. Pack
in an airtight
container and
freeze for up to
2 months. Thaw
thoroughly before
cooking.

Prawns with Ginger

Protein packed

Fuller for longer

Extra low sat fat

Super low calorie

Wheat, gluten & dairy free

 SERVES 4

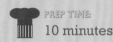 PREP TIME: 10 minutes

 COOKING TIME: 25–30 minutes

nutritional information per serving	180 kcals, 9g fat, 1.5g sat fat, 7.5g total sugars, 2.4g salt, 3g fibre, 10g carbs, 22g protein

Selenium-and zinc-rich prawns and plant compounds in the ginger give this dish huge immune-boosting powers.

INGREDIENTS

1 tsp chopped fresh ginger

1 tsp crushed fresh garlic

1 tsp salt

1 tsp chilli powder

2 tbsp lemon juice

3 tbsp oil

3 onions, chopped

1 green pepper, sliced

400 g/14 oz canned chopped tomatoes

350 g/12 oz cooked, peeled prawns

fresh coriander leaves, to garnish

boiled rice, to serve

1. Place the ginger, garlic, salt and chilli powder in a small bowl and mix to combine. Add the lemon juice and mix to form a paste.

2. Heat the oil in a saucepan. Add the onions and green pepper and fry until browned.

3. Add the spice paste to the onions, reduce the heat to low and cook, stirring and mixing well, for about 3 minutes. Add the tomatoes and cook for 5–7 minutes, stirring occasionally.

4. Add the prawns to the pan and cook for 10 minutes, stirring occasionally. Garnish with fresh coriander and serve with rice.

Thai Fish Curry

Low on carbs

Protein packed

Fuller for longer

Super low calorie

Wheat, gluten & dairy free

 SERVES 4

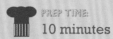 PREP TIME: 10 minutes

 COOKING TIME: 20–25 minutes

nutritional information per serving	248 kcals, 8.5g fat, 4g sat fat, 0.9g total sugars, 0.3g salt, 0.5g fibre, 1.1g carbs, 42g protein

Here's an easy yet delicious way to enjoy white fish – the Thai spices add masses of flavour without calories.

INGREDIENTS

1 tbsp oil

2 spring onions, sliced

1 tsp cumin seeds, ground

2 fresh green chillies, chopped

1 tsp coriander seeds, ground

4 tbsp chopped fresh coriander

1 tsp chopped fresh mint

1 tbsp snipped fresh chives

150 ml/5 fl oz light coconut milk

4 white fish fillets, about 225 g/8 oz each

salt and pepper

1 tsp chopped fresh mint, to garnish

cooked basmati rice, to serve

1. Heat the oil in a large frying pan or shallow saucepan and add the spring onions. Fry the spring onions over a medium heat until they are softened but not coloured.

2. Stir in the cumin, chillies and ground coriander, and cook until fragrant. Add the fresh coriander, mint, chives and coconut milk and season to taste with salt and pepper.

3. Carefully place the fish fillets in the pan and poach for 10–15 minutes, or until the flesh flakes when tested with a fork.

4. Garnish the curry with the chopped mint and serve immediately, with the basmati rice on the side.

1

2

3

Low on carbs

Fuller for longer

Super low calorie

Wheat, gluten
& dairy free

Grilled Salmon with Mango & Lime Salsa

 SERVES 4

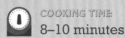 PREP TIME:
15 minutes

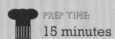 COOKING TIME:
8–10 minutes

nutritional information per serving	290 kcals, 17.5g fat, 6g sat fat, 9g total sugars, 0.1g salt, 3g fibre, 10g carbs, 24g protein

The refreshing, clean flavours of mango and lime are good with oily fish like salmon.

INGREDIENTS

2 tbsp lime juice

1 tbsp clear honey

1 tbsp chopped fresh dill

4 salmon fillets, about 115 g/4 oz each

salt and pepper

boiled new potatoes and salad leaves, to serve (optional)

salsa

1 ripe mango, peeled, stoned and diced

finely grated rind and juice of 1 lime

2 tbsp desiccated coconut

1 tbsp chopped fresh dill

1. Preheat a grill to high and lay a piece of foil on a grill pan. Mix together the lime juice, honey and dill in a wide dish. Season to taste with salt and pepper.

2. Place the salmon fillets in the dish and turn to coat evenly in the glaze. Arrange on the prepared grill pan and grill for 4–5 minutes on each side, turning once, or until cooked through.

3. Meanwhile, prepare the salsa. Mix the mango in a small bowl with the lime rind and juice. Stir in the coconut and dill.

4. Serve the salmon hot, with the salsa spooned over the top and new potatoes and salad leaves alongside, if desired.

1

2

3

COOK'S NOTE
Prick a fresh
lime and
microwave it on
high for 30
seconds to get
much more juice
from it.

Fish Tacos with Avocado Salsa

 SERVES 4   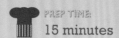 PREP TIME: 15 minutes   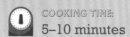 COOKING TIME: 5–10 minutes

nutritional information per serving	300 kcals, 14g fat, 1g sat fat, 3g total sugars, 1.3g salt, 3.5g fibre, 22g carbs, 22g protein

The warm and inviting tastes of Mexico make this quick, high-nutrient supper a real treat.

INGREDIENTS

salsa
½ red onion, diced
2 jalapeño peppers, deseeded and diced
2 tomatoes, diced
½ avocado, diced
2 tbsp chopped fresh coriander
3 tbsp lime juice
½ tsp salt

fish
2 tbsp lime juice
1 tbsp olive oil
1 tsp ground cumin
1 tsp chilli powder
½ tsp salt
400 g/14 oz white fish fillets

to serve
8 small corn tortillas (25 g/1 oz each)
300 g/10½ oz red cabbage, shredded

1. Put all the salsa ingredients in a medium bowl and stir to mix well.

2. Preheat a grill to medium–high or put a griddle pan over a medium–high heat. In a small bowl, combine the lime juice, olive oil, cumin, chilli powder and salt.

3. Brush the lime mixture on both sides of the fish fillets. Grill the fish over a medium–high heat for about 2–4 minutes per side or until grill marks start to appear and the fish is opaque and cooked through. Chop the fish into bite-sized chunks.

4. To serve, warm the tortillas under the grill, then top them with the fish, salsa and shredded cabbage. Serve immediately.

1

2

3

Halibut with Romesco Sauce

Low on carbs

Protein packed

Fuller for longer

Extra low sat fat

Super low calorie

 SERVES 4

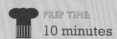 PREP TIME: 10 minutes

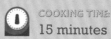 COOKING TIME: 15 minutes

nutritional information per serving	261 kcals, 7g fat, 1g sat fat, 4.5g total sugars, 1.4g salt, 1.7g fibre, 10g carbs, 40g protein

High in protein, low in fat and with a fine flavour, halibut balances well with a rich Mediterranean sauce.

INGREDIENTS

675 g/1 lb 8 oz halibut fillets
¾ tsp salt
½ tsp pepper
green vegetables, to serve

sauce
1 large red pepper
3 garlic cloves
25 g/1 oz flaked, toasted almonds
1 thick slice of bread, torn into a few pieces
1 tsp salt
1 tsp paprika
250g/9 oz canned chopped tomatoes
2 tbsp red wine vinegar

1. To make the sauce, preheat the grill. Quarter the pepper and place the pieces, cut-side down, on a baking sheet along with the garlic cloves. Grill, turning the garlic once, until the garlic is browned and soft and the skin of the pepper blackens and blisters. Remove from the grill and set aside to cool slightly.

2. When cool enough to handle, peel the blackened skin from the pepper and remove the core and seeds, discarding both. Put the pepper and garlic in a food processor along with the almonds, bread, salt and paprika. Process to a paste. Add the tomatoes and vinegar and process until the tomatoes are smooth and fully incorporated.

3. To cook the fish, preheat a grill to high or heat a griddle pan over a high heat. Season the fish with the salt and pepper and grill for about 4 minutes. Turn and grill on the second side for about a further 4 minutes or until the fish is opaque and cooked through. Serve the fish immediately, with the sauce drizzled over it and green vegetables.

1

2

3

GOES WELL WITH
This goes well with a portion of skin-on, steamed new potatoes, garnished with a drizzle of olive oil.

Protein packed

Fuller for longer

Extra low sat fat

Super low calorie

Chipotle-lime Prawn Burgers

 SERVES 4

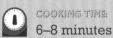 PREP TIME:
10–15 minutes

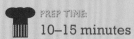 COOKING TIME:
6–8 minutes

nutritional information per serving	300 kcals, 7.5g fat, 1.1g sat fat, 2g total sugars, 3.3g salt, 3.5g fibre, 31g carbs, 31g protein

This light burger makes a fantastic change from meat varieties and is very low in saturated fat.

INGREDIENTS

550 g/1 lb 4 oz cooked, peeled prawns

1 celery stick, finely diced

2 spring onions, finely chopped

2 tbsp finely chopped fresh coriander

1 garlic clove, finely chopped

½ tsp salt

½ tsp ground chipotle

zest and juice of 1 lime

2 tsp olive oil

2 tbsp light mayonnaise

4 small wholemeal burger buns, toasted

4 lettuce leaves

1. Process 450 g/1 lb of the prawns in a food processor. Dice the remaining 100 g/4 oz of prawns. In a medium bowl, combine the puréed and diced prawns. Add the celery, spring onions, coriander, garlic, salt, ground chipotle and lime zest and juice and mix well.

2. Form the prawn mixture into four burgers. Heat the oil in a large frying pan over a medium–high heat. Add the prawn burgers and cook for about 3–4 minutes or until browned underneath. Flip the burgers over and cook for a further 3–4 minutes, or until browned and cooked through.

3. Spread the mayonnaise onto the lower halves of the buns, dividing evenly. Place one prawn burger on the lower half of each bun, then top with a lettuce leaf and the top half of the bun. Serve immediately.

1

1

2

COOK'S NOTE
Chipotle is a smoked
dried jalapeño chilli —
but if you can't get it,
use smoked paprika
instead.

Protein packed

Fuller for longer

Extra low sat fat

Super low calorie

Chunky Monkfish Hotpot

 SERVES 4

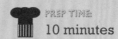 PREP TIME:
10 minutes

 COOKING TIME:
20–25 minutes

nutritional information per serving	250 kcals, 7g fat, 1g sat fat, 7g total sugars, 0.5g salt, 3g fibre, 16g carbs, 27g protein

Colourful and flavourful, this seafood hotpot cooks in record time, perfect for easy and informal entertaining.

INGREDIENTS

2 tbsp olive oil

1 onion, thinly sliced

1 large yellow pepper, deseeded and thinly sliced

1 celery stick, sliced

300 ml/10 fl oz fish stock

400 g/14 oz canned chopped tomatoes

200 g/7 oz fresh or canned sweetcorn

500 g/1 lb 2 oz monkfish fillet, cut into chunks

8 raw, peeled and deveined tiger prawns

salt and pepper

gremolata

finely grated rind of 1 lemon

2 tbsp finely chopped fresh flat-leaf parsley

1 garlic clove, finely chopped

1. Heat the oil in a large, flameproof casserole over a medium heat and fry the onion, pepper and celery, stirring occasionally, for about 10 minutes, or until softened but not brown.

2. Add the fish stock and tomatoes and bring to the boil. Stir in the sweetcorn, season to taste with salt and pepper, then add the chunks of monkfish and bring back to the boil. Place the prawns on top.

3. Reduce the heat to low and leave to simmer gently for about 10 minutes, or until the fish is firm and the prawns have turned pink.

4. Meanwhile, prepare the gremolata by mixing together the lemon rind, parsley and garlic in a small bowl.

5. Sprinkle the gremolata over the hotpot and serve immediately.

Low on carbs

Protein packed

Fuller for longer

Extra low sat fat

Super low calorie

Rustic Fish Casserole

 SERVES 4

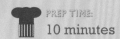 PREP TIME:
10 minutes

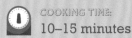 COOKING TIME:
10–15 minutes

nutritional information per serving	230 kcals, 8g fat, 1g sat fat, 6g total sugars, 1.4g salt, 2.8g fibre, 8g carbs, 30.5g protein

A bowl of steaming fish stew with crusty bread is a meal that is very quick and easy to rustle up.

INGREDIENTS

300 g/10½ oz live clams, scrubbed
2 tbsp olive oil
1 large onion, chopped
2 garlic cloves, crushed
2 celery sticks, sliced
350 g/12 oz firm white fish fillet
250 g/9 oz prepared squid rings
400 ml/14 fl oz fish stock
6 plum tomatoes, chopped
small bunch of fresh thyme
salt and pepper
crusty bread, to serve

1. Discard any clams with broken shells and any that refuse to close when tapped.

2. Heat the oil in a large frying pan over a medium heat. Add the onion, garlic and celery and cook for 3–4 minutes, stirring occasionally until softened but not browned. Meanwhile, cut the fish into chunks.

3. Stir the fish and squid into the pan, then fry gently for 2 minutes. Stir in the stock, tomatoes and thyme with salt and pepper to taste. Cover and simmer gently for 3–4 minutes. Add the clams, cover and cook over a high heat for a further 2 minutes, or until the shells open. Discard any that remain closed.

4. Transfer to warmed serving bowls and serve immediately with crusty bread.

2

3

3

SOMETHING
DIFFERENT
Try mussels instead
of clams for a change.
For the white fish,
monkfish or seabass
are ideal to use too.

Extra low sat fat

Super low calorie

Prawn & Sausage Jambalaya

 SERVES 6   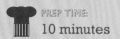 PREP TIME: 10 minutes   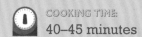 COOKING TIME: 40–45 minutes

nutritional information per serving	270 kcals, 6g fat, 2g sat fat, 5g total sugars, 1.8g salt, 2g fibre, 27g carbs, 20g protein

Prawns and spicy sausage are a heavenly combination, and this dish is low in both fat and calories!

INGREDIENTS

1 tbsp olive oil

1 onion, diced

2 garlic cloves, finely chopped

1 green pepper, deseeded and diced

2 celery sticks, diced

160 g/5¾ oz long-grain white rice

1 tbsp paprika

2 tsp dried oregano

2 tsp dried thyme

1 tsp salt

½ tsp cayenne pepper, or to taste

½ tsp pepper

400 g/14 oz canned chopped tomatoes

700 ml/1¼ pints chicken stock

1 bay leaf

450 g/1 lb cooked, peeled prawns

115 g/4 oz Andouille sausage or spicy Italian sausage, cooked and diced

1. Heat the oil in a large, heavy-based saucepan over a medium–high heat. Add the onion, garlic, green pepper and celery and cook, stirring occasionally, for about 5 minutes or until soft.

2. Add the rice, paprika, oregano, thyme, salt, cayenne and pepper and cook for about a further 30 seconds. Add the tomatoes, stock and bay leaf. Reduce the heat to medium, cover and cook, stirring occasionally, for about 25–30 minutes or until the rice is tender.

3. Stir in the prawns and sausage and cook, uncovered, for about 6–8 minutes or until the prawns and sausage are warmed through. Remove and discard the bay leaf. Serve immediately.

Sweet & Sour Noodles *168*

Spicy Black-eyed Beans *170*

Butternut Squash & Lentil Stew *172*

Spicy Ciabatta Pizza *174*

Bean Burgers *176*

Spicy Sweetcorn Chowder *178*

Tofu Steak with Fennel & Orange *180*

Stuffed Tomatoes *182*

Broccoli Pizza *184*

Mixed Bean Chilli *186*

Lentil Dal *188*

Polenta Tart with Herb Crust *190*

Mushroom Risotto *192*

Tempeh Noodle Bowl *194*

Tofu Moussaka *196*

Pasta with Tomato & Basil Sauce *198*

Warm Chickpea & Halloumi Salad *200*

Roast Butternut Squash *202*

Aubergine Tagine with Polenta *204*

Stir-fried Rice with Green Vegetables *206*

Spanish Tortilla *208*

Tagliatelle with Hazelnut Pesto *210*

Tofu Stir-fry *212*

Baked Root Vegetable & Rosemary Cake *214*

Vegetable Mains

Extra low sat fat

Super low calorie

Sweet & Sour Noodles

 SERVES 4

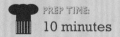 PREP TIME:
10 minutes

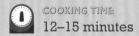 COOKING TIME:
12–15 minutes

nutritional information per serving	254 kcals, 6g fat, 1.5g sat fat, 13.5g total sugars, 2.3g salt, 3.5g fibre, 40g carbs, 7g protein

These Chinese-style noodles make a brilliant vegetarian supper, with masses of flavour and vitamin C.

INGREDIENTS

140 g/5 oz dried medium egg noodles

2 tsp sunflower oil

1 large red pepper, deseeded and thinly sliced

150 g/5½ oz beansprouts

5 spring onions, thinly sliced

3 tbsp Chinese rice wine or dry sherry

salt

sauce

3 tbsp light soy sauce

2 tbsp clear honey

2 tbsp tomato purée

2 tsp cornflour

2 tsp sesame oil

125 ml/4 fl oz vegetable stock

1. Bring a large saucepan of lightly salted water to the boil. Add the noodles, bring back to the boil and cook according to the instructions on the packet until tender but still firm to the bite. Drain.

2. To make the sauce, put the soy sauce, honey, tomato purée, cornflour and sesame oil into a small bowl and mix together until smooth, then stir in the stock.

3. Heat the sunflower oil in a large wok or heavy-based frying pan. Add the red pepper and stir-fry for 4 minutes until soft. Add the beansprouts and stir-fry for 1 minute. Add the noodles and spring onions, then pour the wine and sauce over the vegetables and noodles. Toss together over the heat for 1–2 minutes until the sauce is bubbling and thickened and the noodles are heated all the way through. Serve immediately.

Fuller for longer

Extra low sat fat

Spicy Black-eyed Beans

 SERVES 4

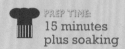 PREP TIME:
15 minutes
plus soaking

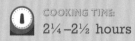 COOKING TIME:
2¼–2½ hours

nutritional information per serving	440 kcals, 4.5g fat, 0.8g sat fat, 22g total sugars, 2.9g salt, 13g fibre, 72g carbs, 23g protein

Black-eyed beans are one of the most flavoursome pulses and this fibre-rich recipe makes the most of them!

INGREDIENTS

350 g/12 oz black-eyed beans, soaked overnight in cold water

1 tbsp vegetable oil

2 onions, chopped

1 tbsp clear honey

2 tbsp treacle

4 tbsp dark soy sauce

1 tsp dry mustard powder

4 tbsp tomato purée

450 ml/16 fl oz vegetable stock

1 bay leaf

1 sprig each of rosemary, thyme and sage

1 small orange

1 tbsp cornflour

2 red peppers, deseeded and diced

pepper

2 tbsp chopped fresh flat-leaf parsley, to garnish

1. Preheat the oven to 150°C/300°F/Gas Mark 2. Rinse the beans and place in a saucepan. Cover with water, bring to the boil and boil rapidly for 10 minutes. Drain and place in an ovenproof casserole dish.

2. Meanwhile, heat the oil in a frying pan and fry the onions for 5 minutes. Stir in the honey, treacle, soy sauce, mustard and tomato purée. Pour in the stock, bring to the boil and pour over the beans.

3. Tie the bay leaf and herbs together with a clean piece of string and add to the beans. Using a vegetable peeler, pare off three pieces of orange rind, mix into the beans, and season to taste with pepper. Cover and cook in the preheated oven for 1 hour.

4. Extract the juice from the orange and blend with the cornflour to form a paste. Stir into the beans along with the red peppers. Cover and cook in the oven for 1 hour, or until the sauce is rich and thick and the beans are tender. Discard the herbs and orange rind. Garnish with chopped parsley and serve immediately.

Fuller for longer

Extra low sat fat

Super low calorie

Wheat, gluten
& dairy free

Butternut Squash & Lentil Stew

 SERVES 4

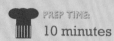 PREP TIME:
10 minutes

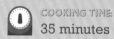 COOKING TIME:
35 minutes

nutritional information per serving	234 kcals, 8g fat, 0.8g sat fat, 9g total sugars, 1.6g salt, 6g fibre, 26.5g carbs, 11g protein

Brown lentils have a meaty flavour and are good for vegetarians, as they are rich in both iron and protein.

INGREDIENTS

1 tbsp olive oil
1 onion, diced
3 garlic cloves, finely chopped
2 tbsp tomato purée
2 tsp ground cumin
1 tsp ground cinnamon
1 tsp salt
¼ tsp cayenne pepper
450 g/1 lb butternut squash, diced
100 g/3½ oz brown lentils
450 ml/16 fl oz gluten-free vegetable stock
1 tbsp lemon juice

to garnish
4 tbsp low-fat natural soya yogurt
2 tbsp finely chopped coriander
2 tbsp flaked almonds

1. Heat the oil in a large saucepan over a medium–high heat. Add the onion and garlic and cook, stirring occasionally, for about 5 minutes or until soft.

2. Add the tomato purée, cumin, cinnamon, salt and cayenne and give it a quick stir. Add the squash, lentils and stock and bring to the boil. Reduce the heat to low and simmer, uncovered, stirring occasionally, for about 25 minutes until the squash and lentils are tender.

3. Just before serving, stir in the lemon juice. Serve hot, garnished with a dollop of the yogurt and a sprinkling of the coriander and almonds.

1

2

3

Super low calorie

Spicy Ciabatta Pizza

 SERVES 4   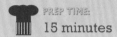 PREP TIME: 15 minutes   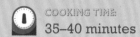 COOKING TIME: 35–40 minutes

nutritional information per serving	349 kcals, 12g fat, 5g sat fat, 10g total sugars, 1.9g salt, 5g fibre, 41g carbs, 18g protein

Pizza is a family favourite and this version is a healthy, nutrient-rich take on the classic margherita.

INGREDIENTS

400 g/14 oz canned chopped tomatoes

1 garlic clove, crushed

1 red pepper, deseeded and chopped

1 green pepper, deseeded and chopped

½ tsp hot smoked paprika

1 ciabatta loaf

200 g/7 oz half-fat mozzarella cheese, thinly sliced

2 tbsp capers in brine, drained, or 12 stoned black olives

1½ tbsp olive oil

½ tsp dried oregano

rocket or basil leaves, to serve

1. Place the tomatoes, garlic, peppers and smoked paprika in a saucepan over a medium heat. Bring to the boil, then reduce the heat and simmer for 20–25 minutes, or until thick and most of the liquid has evaporated.

2. Preheat the oven to 220°C/425°F/Gas Mark 7. Slice the loaf in half lengthways and place the two pieces cut sides up on a baking sheet. Spread with the tomato sauce, then top with the mozzarella slices and capers or olives.

3. Mix the olive oil and oregano together and drizzle over the top of the loaves. Bake in the preheated oven for 10–12 minutes, or until crisp and brown around the edges and the cheese is melted and bubbling. Serve immediately, scattered with rocket or basil leaves.

Bean Burgers

Fuller for longer

Extra low sat fat

Super low calorie

 SERVES 4

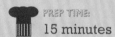 PREP TIME:
15 minutes

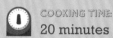 COOKING TIME:
20 minutes

nutritional information
per serving

111 kcals, 4g fat, 0.5g sat fat, 3.5g total sugars, 0.6g salt, 6g fibre, 13g carbs, 5g protein

Satisfy your appetite with these great tasting home-made burgers that will taste far better than those you buy.

INGREDIENTS

1 tbsp sunflower oil,
plus extra for brushing

1 onion, finely chopped

1 garlic clove, finely chopped

1 tsp ground coriander

1 tsp ground cumin

115 g/4 oz white mushrooms,
finely chopped

425 g/15 oz canned borlotti or
red kidney beans, drained
and rinsed

2 tbsp chopped fresh
flat-leaf parsley

plain flour, for dusting

salt and pepper

hamburger buns and salad,
to serve

1. Heat the oil in a heavy-based frying pan over a medium heat. Add the onion and cook, stirring frequently, for 5 minutes, or until softened. Add the garlic, coriander and cumin and cook, stirring, for a further minute. Add the mushrooms and cook, stirring frequently, for 4–5 minutes until all the liquid has evaporated. Transfer to a bowl.

2. Put the beans in a small bowl and mash with a fork. Stir into the mushroom mixture with the parsley and season with salt and pepper.

3. Preheat the grill to medium–high. Divide the mixture equally into four portions, dust lightly with flour and shape into flat, round burgers. Brush with oil and cook under the grill for 4–5 minutes on each side. Serve in hamburger buns with salad.

BE PREPARED
These will freeze well so make a double batch. Open freeze on a tray then transfer to a rigid container. Freeze for up to 3 months. Cook from frozen.

Spicy Sweetcorn Chowder

Fuller for longer

Extra low sat fat

Super low calorie

Wheat, gluten & dairy free

 SERVES 6

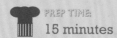 PREP TIME:
15 minutes

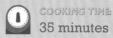 COOKING TIME:
35 minutes

nutritional information **per serving**

156 kcals, 8g fat, 1g sat fat, 7g total sugars, 0.7g salt, 4g fibre, 20g carbs, 8g protein

A meal in a bowl, this chowder packs in a huge variety of vegetables which will keep you full for hours!

INGREDIENTS

1 tbsp olive oil

1 onion, diced

2 garlic cloves, finely chopped

2 carrots, diced

2 celery sticks, diced

1 red pepper, deseeded and diced

450 g/1 lb frozen sweetcorn

¾ tsp salt

½ tsp chilli powder

1 litre/1¾ pints gluten-free vegetable stock

225 g/8 oz silken tofu, drained

2 tbsp chopped fresh coriander, to garnish

3 spring onions, thinly sliced, to garnish

1. Heat the oil in a large frying pan over a medium–high heat. Add the onion and garlic and cook, stirring occasionally, for about 5 minutes or until soft.

2. Add the carrots, celery, pepper, sweetcorn, salt, chilli powder and stock. Bring to the boil, reduce the heat to medium–low and simmer, uncovered, for about 20 minutes or until the vegetables are soft.

3. In a blender or food processor, purée the tofu with a ladleful of the soup. Stir the purée into the soup and simmer for about 5 minutes or until heated through. Serve hot, garnished with the coriander and spring onions.

1

2

3

BE PREPARED
Buy peppers in season, then dice, bag and freeze them so you'll always have some to hand!

Fuller for longer

Extra low sat fat

Super low calorie

Wheat, gluten
& dairy free

Tofu Steak with Fennel & Orange

 SERVES 4

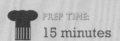 PREP TIME:
15 minutes

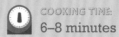 COOKING TIME:
6–8 minutes

nutritional information per serving	141 kcals, 8g fat, 1g sat fat, 6g total sugars, 0.2g salt, 3g fibre, 8g carbs, 10g protein

Tofu is easy to infuse with spicy flavours so it is ideal for using with hot spices, such as Moroccan harissa or Cajun seasoning.

INGREDIENTS

350 g/12 oz extra firm tofu, drained
1 tbsp gluten-free harissa paste
2 tsp extra virgin olive oil
1 large orange
1 fennel bulb, very thinly sliced
1 small red onion, thinly sliced
8 stoned black olives, halved
chopped fresh mint, to garnish

1. Preheat the grill to high. Place the tofu on a clean tea towel and press lightly to remove any excess moisture.

2. Cut the tofu into four thick triangles. Mix the harissa with the oil. Brush this mixture over the tofu.

3. Lift the tofu steaks onto a baking sheet and cook under the preheated grill for 6–8 minutes, turning once, until golden brown.

4. Meanwhile, use a sharp knife to cut all the rind and white pith from the orange and carefully remove the segments from the membranes, catching the juice in a bowl.

5. Place the orange segments, fennel, onion and olives in bowl. Mix thoroughly to combine and then divide the mixture between four serving plates.

6. Place the tofu steaks on top, drizzle with the reserved orange juice and garnish with chopped fresh mint to serve.

3

4

5

Extra low sat fat

Super low calorie

Wheat, gluten
& dairy free

Stuffed Tomatoes

 SERVES 4

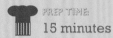 PREP TIME:
15 minutes

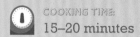 COOKING TIME:
15–20 minutes

nutritional information per serving	253 kcals, 11g fat, 1g sat fat, 13g total sugars, trace salt, 3g fibre, 37g carbs, 5g protein

These light and tasty rice-filled tomatoes make an ideal summer meal. Half quantities also make a great starter.

INGREDIENTS

4 beef tomatoes
300 g/10½ oz cooked rice
8 spring onions, chopped
3 tbsp chopped fresh mint
2 tbsp chopped fresh flat-leaf parsley
3 tbsp pine nuts
3 tbsp raisins
2 tsp olive oil
salt and pepper

1. Cut the tomatoes in half, then scoop out the seeds and discard.

2. Stand the tomatoes upside down on kitchen paper for a few moments in order for the juices to drain out.

3. Preheat the oven to 190°C/375°F/Gas Mark 5. Turn the tomatoes the right way up and sprinkle the insides with salt and pepper.

4. Mix together the rice, spring onions, mint, parsley, pine nuts and raisins in a bowl. Spoon the mixture into the tomato cups.

5. Drizzle over a little olive oil, then arrange the tomatoes on a baking sheet or baking dish. Cook in the preheated oven for 15–20 minutes, or until they are tender and cooked through.

6. Transfer the tomatoes to serving plates and serve immediately.

1

4

4

Broccoli Pizza

Super low calorie

 SERVES 8

 PREP TIME:
20 minutes
plus rising

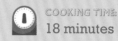 COOKING TIME:
18 minutes

nutritional information per serving	274 kcals, 9g fat, 4g sat fat, 2g total sugars, 1.3g salt, 3g fibre, 40.5g carbs, 11g protein

One secret to healthier pizza is to have vegetables in the topping – and our broccoli version certainly achieves that!

INGREDIENTS

250 ml/9 fl oz lukewarm water

1½ tsp easy-blend dried yeast

2 tsp salt

1 tsp sugar

1 tbsp olive oil

400 g/14 oz strong white flour, plus extra for dusting

2 sprays olive oil spray

topping

150 g/5½ oz small broccoli florets

2 tsp olive oil

1 red onion, thinly sliced

1 garlic clove, finely chopped

1 tbsp chopped fresh oregano

140 g/5 oz Emmenthal cheese, grated

¼–½ tsp chilli flakes

1. To make the pizza base, combine the lukewarm water, yeast, salt and sugar in a large mixing bowl and stir well. Leave for about 10 minutes or until bubbly. Stir in the olive oil, then gradually mix in the flour with an electric whisk or food processor until the mixture comes together in a ball. Turn the dough out on to a lightly floured surface and knead, adding a little more flour if needed, for a minute or two or until firm. Wash and dry the mixing bowl, then spray with olive oil. Put the dough in the bowl, cover with clingfilm and leave to rise in a warm place for about an hour, or until doubled in size.

2. Preheat the oven to 230°C/450°F/Gas Mark 8. Spray a baking sheet with olive oil. Roll out the dough into a large rectangle and place it on the prepared baking sheet. Bake in the preheated oven for about 8 minutes or until just beginning to brown.

3. Meanwhile, put the broccoli in a microwave-safe bowl along with 4 tablespoons of water and cover tightly with clingfilm. Microwave on high for about 3 minutes or until the broccoli is just tender. Drain and chop the broccoli into small pieces.

4. Heat the olive oil in a frying pan over a medium heat. Add the onion and garlic. Cook, stirring occasionally, for about 5 minutes or until soft. Remove from the heat and stir in the oregano. Spread the onion mixture evenly onto the part-baked pizza base and top it with the broccoli, then sprinkle with the cheese and chilli flakes. Bake for about 10 minutes or until the cheese is melted, bubbling and golden brown. Slice and serve immediately.

1

4

4

Fuller for longer

Extra low sat fat

Super low calorie

Mixed Bean Chilli

 SERVES 5

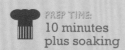 PREP TIME:
10 minutes
plus soaking

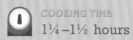 COOKING TIME:
1¼–1½ hours

nutritional information per serving	113 kcals, 0.7g fat, 0.1g sat fat, 4.5g total sugars, 0.1g salt, 8g fibre, 18g carbs, 9g protein

An incredibly easy-to-cook bowlful of tasty goodness, ideal for a cold winter evening.

INGREDIENTS

200 g/7 oz dried mixed beans, such as kidney, soya, pinto, cannellini and chickpeas

1 red onion, diced

1 garlic clove, crushed

1 tbsp hot chilli powder

400 g/14 oz canned chopped tomatoes

1 tbsp tomato purée

4 tbsp low-fat natural yogurt, to garnish

soft flour tortilla wraps, to serve

1. Soak the beans overnight or for 8 hours in a large bowl of cold water. Drain, rinse and put the beans into a large saucepan. Cover with cold water, then bring to the boil and boil rapidly for 10 minutes. Reduce the heat, cover and simmer for a further 45 minutes, or until tender. Drain.

2. Put the cooked beans, onion, garlic, chilli powder, tomatoes and tomato purée into a saucepan and bring to the boil. Reduce the heat, cover and simmer for 20–25 minutes, or until the onion is tender.

3. Ladle the chilli into bowls and top each bowl with some of the yogurt. Serve immediately with soft flour tortilla wraps.

1

1

2

COOK'S NOTE
To save time, use canned pulses, drained and rinsed, and omit step one - two 400 g /14 oz tins will be equivalent.

Lentil Dal

Fuller for longer

Extra low sat fat

Super low calorie

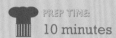 SERVES 4

 PREP TIME: 10 minutes

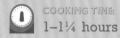 COOKING TIME: 1–1¼ hours

nutritional information per serving	252 cals, 7g fat, 1g sat fat, 4g total sugars, 1.3g salt, 6g fibre, 37g carbs, 13g protein

This is a perfect combination of high protein and high fibre pulses, healthy oils and antioxidant-rich spices.

INGREDIENTS

225 g/8 oz chang dal or yellow split peas, washed

½ tsp ground turmeric

1 tsp ground coriander

1 tsp salt

4 curry leaves

2 tbsp oil

½ tsp asafoetida powder (optional)

1 tsp cumin seeds

2 onions, chopped

2 garlic cloves, crushed

1-cm/½-inch piece fresh ginger, grated

½ tsp garam masala

1. Put the chang dal in a large saucepan. Pour in enough water to cover by 2.5 cm/1 inch.

2. Bring to the boil and use a spoon to remove any of the foam that has formed.

3. Add the turmeric, ground coriander, salt and curry leaves. Simmer for 1 hour. The chang dal should be tender, but not mushy.

4. Heat the oil in a balti pan or wok. Add the asafoetida (if using) and fry for 30 seconds. Add the cumin seeds and fry until they start popping. Add the onions and fry until golden brown.

5. Add the garlic, ginger, garam masala and chang dal mixture to the pan or wok and cook for 2 minutes. Serve immediately.

2

4

5

COOK'S NOTE
If you can't find asafoetida powder, try using celery salt as a substitute.

Polenta Tart with Herb Crust

 SERVES 4

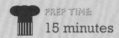 PREP TIME:
15 minutes

 COOKING TIME:
20–25 minutes

nutritional information per serving	300 kcals, 7g fat, 2g sat fat, 5g total sugars, 0.2g salt, 4g fibre, 52g carbs, 7g protein

This polenta tart makes a change from pastry or pizza dough – and it's gluten free, too!

INGREDIENTS

olive oil, for greasing and brushing

850 ml/1½ pints boiling water

250 g/9 oz quick-cook polenta

1 tbsp chopped fresh oregano, plus extra to garnish

1 small yellow pepper, deseeded and thinly sliced

1 small red onion, thinly sliced

1 small courgette, thinly sliced

2 tomatoes, sliced

100 g/3½ oz half-fat mozzarella cheese, diced

8 black olives, stoned and halved

salt and pepper

1. Preheat the oven to 200°C/400°F/Gas Mark 6. Grease a large baking sheet. Pour the water into a large pan, add a pinch of salt, and bring to the boil over a high heat. Add the polenta in a steady stream, stirring constantly until smooth.

2. Reduce the heat and stir constantly for 4–5 minutes, or until the polenta is thick and smooth. Remove from the heat and stir in the oregano. Season to taste with pepper. Spoon the polenta onto the prepared baking sheet and spread out in a 30-cm/12-inch round, raising the edges slightly.

3. Arrange the pepper, onion, courgette and tomatoes over the polenta and add the mozzarella. Top the tart with the olives and brush lightly with olive oil.

4. Bake in the preheated oven for 15–20 minutes, or until bubbling and golden brown. Garnish with oregano and serve immediately.

Mushroom Risotto

 SERVES 1 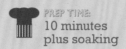 PREP TIME: 10 minutes plus soaking 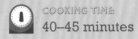 COOKING TIME: 40–45 minutes

nutritional information per serving	435 kcals, 11.4g fat, 4.5g sat fat, 5g total sugars, 0.7g salt, 7g fibre, 51g carbs, 16g protein

A healthier take on the classic Italian risotto, with much less saturated fat.

INGREDIENTS

1 tbsp dried porcini mushrooms

1 tsp olive oil

1 tsp butter

½ onion, finely chopped

1 small garlic clove, finely chopped

150 g/5½ oz mixed fresh mushrooms (e.g. chestnut, shiitake, button)

60 g/2¼ oz arborio or other risotto rice

200 ml/7 fl oz vegetable stock

50 ml/2 fl oz dry white wine or extra stock (optional)

1 small courgette, chopped

1 tsp chopped fresh flat-leaf parsley

1 tsp freshly grated Parmesan cheese

pepper

1. Put the dried mushrooms in a bowl, cover with water, and allow to soak for 30 minutes.

2. About 5 minutes before the soaking time is up, heat the oil and butter in a large, lidded frying pan and sauté the onion and garlic over a medium heat for about 5 minutes, or until soft. Add the fresh mushrooms and some pepper, stir well and cook for 1–2 minutes.

3. Add the rice and soaked mushrooms with their soaking water, stock and wine, if using, and stir. Cover and simmer for 20 minutes, adding a little extra stock or water if it looks dry. Add the courgette and continue to simmer for a further 10 minutes.

4. When the rice is tender and creamy, stir in the parsley and cheese. Serve immediately.

Tempeh Noodle Bowl

Fuller for longer

Extra low sat fat

Super low calorie

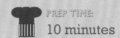 SERVES 4

PREP TIME:
10 minutes

COOKING TIME:
7–10 minutes

nutritional information per serving	250 kcals, 4g fat, 0.5g sat fat, 3g total sugars, 0.8g salt, 2.5g fibre, 42g carbs, 11g protein

Tempeh has an even higher protein content than tofu and is naturally cholesterol free.

INGREDIENTS

125 g/4½ oz shiitake mushrooms

35 g/1¼ oz miso paste

600 ml/1 pint boiling water

175 g/6 oz mangetout, halved diagonally

200 g/7 oz tempeh or smoked tofu, cubed

1 bunch spring onions, sliced

175 g/6 oz dried udon or soba noodles

salt

1. Remove the stems from the mushrooms and cut a deep cross in the top of the caps.

2. Place the miso and water in a large saucepan and stir thoroughly to dissolve the miso. Place the pan over a high heat and bring back to the boil. Add the mushrooms and mangetout and cook for 2–3 minutes to soften. Stir the tempeh and spring onions into the pan and cook for another 2 minutes.

3. Meanwhile, cook the noodles in a saucepan of lightly salted boiling water for 3–4 minutes, or cook according to the packet instructions, until tender. Drain well, then divide between four warmed serving bowls.

4. Spoon the tempeh and vegetable mixture over the noodles and serve immediately.

COOK'S NOTE
If you can buy
fresh udon or
soba noodles,
these take only
1-2 minutes
to cook.

Fuller for longer

Extra low sat fat

Super low calorie

Tofu Moussaka

 SERVES 4   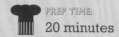 PREP TIME: 20 minutes   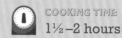 COOKING TIME: 1½–2 hours

nutritional information per serving	273 kcals, 9.5g fat, 2.7g sat fat, 16g total sugars, 0.3g salt, 4.5g fibre, 31g carbs, 16g protein

Who doesn't love the delicious indulgence of moussaka? And the good news is that this is also a low-fat treat!

INGREDIENTS

150 g/5½ oz baking potatoes, scrubbed

4 tbsp lemon juice

1 tsp rapeseed or vegetable oil

1 tsp sugar

2 tsp crushed garlic

1 tsp ground cumin

2 tbsp dried oregano

250 g/9 oz aubergine, diced

100 g/3½ oz onion, sliced

175 g/6 oz mixed peppers, deseeded and diced

200 g/7 oz canned chopped tomatoes

400 g/14 oz natural yogurt

2 tbsp cornflour

2 tbsp English mustard powder

200 g/7 oz silken tofu (drained weight), sliced

85 g/3 oz beef tomato, thinly sliced

pepper

1. Preheat the oven to 190°C/375°F/Gas Mark 5. Bake the potatoes in their skins in the oven for 45 minutes, then remove and leave to cool. Cut into thin slices.

2. Mix the lemon juice, oil, sugar, garlic, cumin and oregano together in a small bowl, then lightly brush over the diced aubergine, reserving the remaining mixture. Spread out on a baking sheet and bake in the preheated oven for 15 minutes. Leave the oven on.

3. Heat the reserved lemon juice mixture in a frying pan over a high heat, add the onion and peppers and cook, stirring occasionally, until lightly browned. Add the canned tomatoes, reduce the heat and simmer for 4 minutes.

4. In a separate saucepan, whisk the yogurt and cornflour together, then bring to the boil, whisking constantly (to prevent the yogurt separating) until the yogurt boils and thickens. When the yogurt has thickened, remove from the heat and whisk in the mustard powder.

5. In an ovenproof dish, make layers of the potatoes, aubergine, onion and pepper mixture and tofu, adding yogurt sauce between each layer. Finish with a layer of beef tomato and top with the remaining yogurt sauce.

6. Bake in the preheated oven for 20–25 minutes, or until golden brown on top. Season with pepper and serve immediately.

2

3

5

Pasta with Tomato & Basil Sauce

 SERVES 4   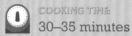 PREP TIME: 15 minutes   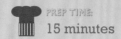 COOKING TIME: 30–35 minutes

nutritional information per serving	351 kcals, 5g fat, 0.8g sat fat, 6g total sugars, trace salt, 5g fibre, 70g carbs, 11.5g protein

This tomato sauce is rich in potassium to help beat fluid retention and high blood pressure.

INGREDIENTS

2 fresh rosemary sprigs

2 garlic cloves, unpeeled

450 g/1 lb tomatoes, halved

1 tbsp olive oil

1 tbsp sun-dried tomato purée

12 fresh basil leaves, plus extra to garnish

675 g/1 lb 8 oz fresh farfalle or 350 g/12 oz dried farfalle

salt and pepper

1. Place the rosemary, garlic and tomatoes, skin side up, in a shallow roasting tin.

2. Preheat the grill to medium. Drizzle with the oil and cook under the preheated grill for 20 minutes, or until the tomato skins are slightly charred.

3. Peel the skin from the tomatoes. Roughly chop the tomato flesh and place in a saucepan. Squeeze the pulp from the garlic cloves and mix with the tomato flesh and sun-dried tomato purée.

4. Roughly tear the fresh basil leaves into smaller pieces and then stir them into the sauce. Season with a little salt and pepper to taste.

5. Place a saucepan of lightly salted water over a high heat and bring to the boil. Add the farfalle, bring back to the boil and cook for 10 minutes, or until tender but still firm to the bite.

6. Gently heat the tomato and basil sauce. Transfer the farfalle to serving plates and garnish with the basil. Serve with the tomato sauce over the top.

1

3

4

Fuller for longer

Super low calorie

Warm Chickpea & Halloumi Salad

 SERVES 4   PREP TIME: 15 minutes   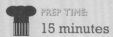 COOKING TIME: 10 minutes

nutritional information per serving	301 kcals, 16.7g fat, 5.5g sat fat, 3.1g total sugars, 2.1g salt, 5.9g fibre, 17.4g carbs, 24g protein

A colourful salad that is rich in protein and fibre, with a full, spicy flavour.

INGREDIENTS

1 tbsp olive oil

1 garlic clove, finely chopped

½ tsp crushed dried chillies

175 g/6 oz baby plum tomatoes, halved

250 g/9 oz light halloumi, diced

1 slice wholemeal bread, cut into 1-cm/½-inch squares

1 tbsp sesame seeds

70 g/2½ oz baby spinach leaves

1 small red onion, thinly sliced

400 g/14 oz canned chickpeas, drained and rinsed

1. Preheat the oven to 200°C/400°F/Gas Mark 6. Mix 2 teaspoons of the olive oil with the garlic, chillies, tomatoes and halloumi in a bowl, stirring to coat evenly. Spread the tomatoes and halloumi over one half of a baking sheet.

2. Place the bread cubes with the remaining oil and sesame seeds in a bowl and stir to coat. Spread the bread cubes on the other half of the sheet.

3. Bake in the preheated oven for about 10 minutes, or until the tomatoes are tender, the halloumi is starting to brown and the bread cubes are crisp.

4. Meanwhile, arrange the spinach leaves in a wide serving dish, or individual dishes, and spoon over the onion and chickpeas.

5. Remove the baking sheet from the oven and spoon the tomatoes, halloumi and bread cubes over the salad. Serve immediately.

1

2

4

SOMETHING DIFFERENT
Replace the chickpeas with canned red kidney beans and omit the halloumi.

Extra low sat fat

Super low calorie

Roast Butternut Squash

 SERVES 4

 PREP TIME:
20 minutes
plus cooling

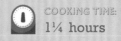 COOKING TIME:
1¼ hours

nutritional information per serving	97 kcals, 0.8g fat, 0.3g sat fat, 11g total sugars, 0.4g salt, 6g fibre, 18g carbs, 5g protein

Squash, stuffed with high-fibre beans and vegetables, is an ideal slimmer's supper, both filling and satisfying.

INGREDIENTS

1 butternut squash, about 450 g/1 lb

1 onion, chopped

2–3 garlic cloves, crushed

4 small tomatoes, chopped

85 g/3 oz chestnut mushrooms, chopped

85 g/3 oz canned butter beans, drained, rinsed and roughly chopped

1 courgette, about 115 g/ 4 oz, trimmed and grated

1 tbsp chopped fresh oregano, plus extra to garnish

2 tbsp tomato purée

300 ml/10 fl oz water

4 spring onions, chopped

1 tbsp Worcestershire or hot pepper sauce, or to taste

pepper

1. Preheat the oven to 190°C/375°F/Gas Mark 5. Prick the squash all over with a metal skewer then roast for 40 minutes, or until tender. Remove from the oven and leave until cool enough to handle.

2. Cut the squash in half, scoop out and discard the seeds then scoop out some of the flesh, making hollows in both halves. Chop the cooked flesh and put in a bowl. Place the two halves side by side in a large roasting tin.

3. Add the onion, garlic, chopped tomatoes and mushrooms to the cooked squash flesh. Add the roughly chopped butter beans, grated courgette, chopped oregano and pepper to taste and mix well. Spoon the filling into the two halves of the squash, packing it down as firmly as possible.

4. Mix the tomato purée with the water, spring onions and Worcestershire sauce in a small bowl and pour around the squash.

5. Cover loosely with a large sheet of foil and bake for 30 minutes, or until piping hot. Serve, divided equally between four warmed plates, garnished with extra chopped oregano.

Fuller for longer

Extra low sat fat

Aubergine Tagine with Polenta

 SERVES 4

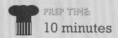 PREP TIME:
10 minutes

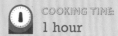 COOKING TIME:
1 hour

nutritional information
per serving

440 kcals, 12g fat, 1.5g sat fat, 16g total sugars, 0.2g salt, 8g fibre, 65g carbs, 12g protein

This tasty Mediterranean tagine has so much flavour, meat eaters won't notice the lack of meat!

INGREDIENTS

1 aubergine, diced

3 tbsp olive oil

1 large onion, thinly sliced

1 carrot, diced

2 garlic cloves, chopped

115 g/4 oz mushrooms, sliced

2 tsp ground coriander

2 tsp cumin seeds

1 tsp chilli powder

1 tsp ground turmeric

600 ml/1 pint canned chopped tomatoes

300 ml/10 fl oz vegetable stock

70 g/2½ oz dried apricots, chopped

400 g/14 oz canned chickpeas, drained and rinsed

2 tbsp coriander, to garnish

polenta

1.2 litres/2 pints hot vegetable stock

200 g/7 oz quick-cook polenta

1. Preheat the grill to medium. Toss the aubergine in 1 tablespoon of the oil and arrange in the grill pan. Cook under the preheated grill for 20 minutes, turning occasionally, until softened and beginning to blacken around the edges – brush with more oil if the aubergine becomes too dry.

2. Heat the remaining oil in a large, heavy-based saucepan over a medium heat. Add the onion and fry, stirring occasionally, for 8 minutes, or until soft and golden. Add the carrot, garlic and mushrooms and cook for 5 minutes. Add the spices and cook, stirring constantly, for a further minute.

3. Add the tomatoes and stock, stir well and bring to the boil. Reduce the heat and simmer for 10 minutes, or until the sauce begins to thicken and reduce.

4. Add the aubergine, apricots and chickpeas, partially cover and cook for a further 10 minutes, stirring occasionally.

5. Meanwhile, to make the polenta, pour the hot stock into a large saucepan and bring to the boil. Pour in the polenta in a steady stream, stirring constantly with a wooden spoon. Reduce the heat to low and cook for 1–2 minutes, or until the polenta thickens to a mashed potato-like consistency. Serve the tagine with the polenta, sprinkled with the fresh coriander.

Extra low sat fat

Super low calorie

Stir-fried Rice with Green Vegetables

 SERVES 4   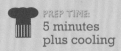 PREP TIME:
5 minutes
plus cooling   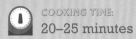 COOKING TIME:
20–25 minutes

nutritional information per serving	288 kcals, 7g fat, 0.8g sat fat, 3g total sugars, 0.2g salt, 2.5g fibre, 45g carbs, 7g protein

Thai basil should not be confused with sweet basil used in many Italian dishes. Thai basil has a slight liquorice flavour which complements this dish perfectly.

INGREDIENTS

225 g/8 oz jasmine rice

2 tbsp vegetable or groundnut oil

1 tbsp green curry paste

6 spring onions, sliced

2 garlic cloves, crushed

1 courgette, cut into thin sticks

115 g/4 oz French beans

175 g/6 oz asparagus, trimmed

3–4 fresh Thai basil leaves

salt

1. Cook the rice in a pan of lightly salted boiling water for 12–15 minutes, drain well, cover, cool thoroughly and chill.

2. Heat the oil in a wok and stir-fry the curry paste for 1 minute. Add the spring onions and garlic and stir-fry for 1 minute.

3. Add the courgette, beans and asparagus and stir-fry for 3–4 minutes, until just tender. Break up the rice and add it to the wok. Cook, stirring constantly for 2–3 minutes, until the rice is hot. Stir in the basil and serve immediately.

1

2

3

FREEZING TIP
Thai basil can be frozen in small quantities. Chop the leaves in a food processor adding a little vegetable oil to coat. Pack into ice cube trays and freeze.

Spanish Tortilla

Fuller for longer

Super low calorie

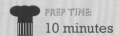 SERVES 4   PREP TIME: 10 minutes   COOKING TIME: 35–40 minutes

nutritional information per serving	258 kcals, 16g fat, 4g sat fat, 2g total sugars, 0.4g salt, 2g fibre, 17g carbs, 13g protein

Eggs, onions and potatoes have never tasted so delicious, and yet our low-cost omelette is easy to make.

INGREDIENTS

350 g/12 oz potatoes, cut into bite-sized cubes

1 tbsp olive oil

15 g/½ oz low-fat spread

1 onion, thinly sliced

6 eggs, lightly beaten

salt and pepper

sliced tomatoes, to serve

1. Cook the potatoes in a saucepan of salted boiling water for 10–12 minutes, or until tender. Drain well and set aside.

2. Meanwhile, heat the oil and spread in a medium-sized frying pan with a heatproof handle over a medium heat. Add the onion and fry, stirring occasionally, for 8 minutes, or until soft and golden. Add the potatoes and cook for a further 5 minutes, stirring to prevent them sticking. Spread the onions and potatoes evenly over the base of the pan.

3. Preheat the grill to medium. Season the eggs to taste with salt and pepper and pour over the onion and potatoes. Cook over a medium heat for 5–6 minutes, or until the eggs are just set and the base of the tortilla is lightly golden.

4. Place the pan under the preheated grill (if the handle is not heatproof, wrap with a double layer of foil) and cook the top of the tortilla for 2–3 minutes until it is just set and risen. Cut into wedges and serve with sliced tomatoes.

HEALTHY HINT
Think about buying organic eggs, which contain higher levels of healthy omega-3 fats.

Tagliatelle with Hazelnut Pesto

 SERVES 4    PREP TIME: 5 minutes   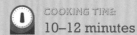 COOKING TIME: 10–12 minutes

nutritional information per serving	522 kcals, 22g fat, 2.5g sat fat, 3g total sugars, 0.1g salt, 9g fibre, 71g carbs, 15g protein

Fresh and light, this protein-packed vegetarian main dish is made in a matter of minutes.

INGREDIENTS

pesto
1 garlic clove, roughly chopped
55 g/2 oz hazelnuts
100 g/3½ oz wild rocket
4 tbsp olive oil
salt and pepper

350 g/12 oz dried tagliatelle
175 g/6 oz fresh or frozen broad beans

1. To make the pesto, place the garlic, hazelnuts, rocket and oil in a food processor and process to a rough paste. Season to taste with salt and pepper.

2. Bring a large pan of lightly salted water to the boil. Add the pasta, return to the boil and cook for 8–10 minutes, or until tender but still firm to the bite. Add the beans 3–4 minutes before the end of the cooking time.

3. Drain the pasta and beans well, then tip back into the pan. Add the pesto and toss to coat evenly. Serve immediately.

GOES WELL WITH

If you can find a vegetarian Parmesan-style cheese, grate a few shavings of this over the pasta to add extra flavour.

Tofu Stir-fry

Low on carbs

Extra low sat fat

Super low calorie

 SERVES 4

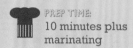 PREP TIME:
10 minutes plus
marinating

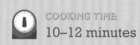 COOKING TIME:
10–12 minutes

nutritional information per serving	120 kcals, 6g fat, 1g sat fat, 5g total sugars, 1.4g salt, 2g fibre, 6g carbs, 9g protein

This vegetable-packed stir-fry is great for anyone on a low-carb diet.

INGREDIENTS

225 g/8 oz firm tofu (drained weight), cut into bite-sized pieces
1 tbsp sunflower oil
2 spring onions, roughly chopped
1 garlic clove, finely chopped
115 g/4 oz baby corn, halved
115 g/4 oz mangetout
115 g/4 oz shiitake mushrooms, thinly sliced
2 tbsp finely chopped fresh coriander leaves, to garnish

marinade
2 tbsp dark soy sauce
1 tbsp Chinese rice wine
2 tsp brown sugar
½ tsp Chinese five-spice powder
1 fresh red chilli, deseeded and finely chopped
2 spring onions, finely chopped
1 tbsp grated fresh ginger

1. Place all the marinade ingredients in a large, shallow, non-metallic dish and stir to mix. Add the bite-sized chunks of tofu and turn them over carefully to coat thoroughly in the marinade. Cover the dish with clingfilm and leave the tofu in the refrigerator to marinate for 2 hours, turning occasionally.

2. Drain the tofu and reserve the marinade. Heat the sunflower oil in a preheated wok or large frying pan. Add the tofu and stir-fry over a medium–high heat for 2–3 minutes, or until golden. Using a slotted spoon, remove the tofu from the wok and reserve. Add the spring onions and garlic and stir-fry for 2 minutes, then add the baby corn and stir-fry for 1 minute. Add the mangetout and mushrooms and stir-fry for a further 2 minutes.

3. Return the tofu to the wok and add the marinade. Cook gently for 1–2 minutes, or until heated through. Garnish with the chopped fresh coriander and serve immediately.

Extra low sat fat

Super low calorie

Wheat, gluten
& dairy free

Baked Root Vegetable & Rosemary Cake

 SERVES 4

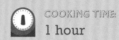 PREP TIME:
15–20 minutes

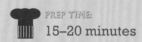 COOKING TIME:
1 hour

nutritional information per serving	104 kcals, 2g fat, 0.3g sat fat, 12g total sugars, 0.2g salt, 11g fibre, 19g carbs, 3g protein

An unusual way to serve a selection of vegetables, subtly flavoured with rosemary and lemon.

INGREDIENTS

olive oil, for greasing

300 g/10½ oz parsnips, roughly grated

300 g/10½ oz carrots, roughly grated

300 g/10½ oz celeriac, roughly grated

1 onion, roughly grated

2 tbsp chopped fresh rosemary

3 tbsp lemon juice

salt and pepper

rosemary sprigs, to garnish

1. Preheat the oven to 190°C/375°F/Gas Mark 5. Grease a 20-cm/ 8-inch springform cake tin and line with baking paper.

2. Place the parsnip, carrot and celeriac in separate, small bowls.

3. Mix together the onion, rosemary and lemon juice in a small bowl. Add a third of the onion mixture to each vegetable bowl, season to taste with salt and pepper, and stir to mix evenly.

4. Spoon the parsnips into the prepared tin, spreading evenly and pressing down lightly. Top with the carrots, press lightly, then add the celeriac.

5. Top the cake with a piece of lightly oiled kitchen foil and press down to condense the contents. Tuck the foil over the edges of the tin to seal. Place on a baking sheet and bake in the preheated oven for about 1 hour, or until tender.

6. Remove the foil and turn out the cake onto a warmed plate. Leave to cool for 5 minutes and then slice and serve, garnished with rosemary sprigs.

Desserts

Coffee Ice Cream

 SERVES 6

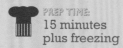 PREP TIME:
15 minutes
plus freezing

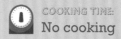 COOKING TIME:
No cooking

nutritional information per serving	150 kcals, 6g fat, 4g sat fat, 18g total sugars, 0.1g salt, 0g fibre, 18g carbs, 4.5g protein

This is a healthier version of ice cream, with much lower levels of saturated fat.

INGREDIENTS

25 g/1 oz plain chocolate

225 g/8 oz ricotta cheese

5 tbsp low-fat natural yogurt

85 g/3 oz caster sugar

175 ml/6 fl oz strong black coffee, cooled and chilled

½ tsp ground cinnamon

dash of vanilla extract

25 g/1 oz chocolate flakes, to decorate

1. Grate the chocolate and reserve. Place the ricotta cheese, yogurt and sugar in a blender or food processor and process until a smooth purée forms. Transfer to a large bowl and beat in the coffee, cinnamon, vanilla extract and grated chocolate.

2. Spoon the mixture into a freezerproof container and freeze for 1½ hours, or until slushy. Remove from the freezer, turn into a bowl and beat. Return to the container and freeze for 1½ hours.

3. Repeat this beating and freezing process twice more before serving in scoops, decorated with chocolate flakes. Alternatively, leave in the freezer until 15 minutes before serving, then transfer to the refrigerator to soften slightly before scooping.

1

2

3

FREEZING TIP
Home-made ice cream tends to harden over time if stored in the freezer too long, but this ice cream will keep well for up to 3 months in a tightly-sealed container.

Pear & Blueberry Strudel

 SERVES 4   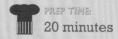 PREP TIME: 20 minutes   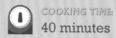 COOKING TIME: 40 minutes

nutritional information per serving	255 kcals, 10g fat, 4g sat fat, 22g total sugars, 0.4g salt, 5g fibre, 32g carbs, 4g protein

Dessert is an ideal occasion to pack fruit into your diet - this strudel provides 1½ portions of your five a day!

INGREDIENTS

25 g/1 oz butter

450 g/1 lb firm ripe Conference pears, cored and chopped

115 g/4 oz blueberries

1 tbsp soft light brown sugar

½ tsp ground cinnamon

1 medium slice wholemeal bread, toasted and torn into pieces

1½ tbsp rapeseed or sunflower oil

4 sheets of filo pastry (each 37 x 28 cm/14½ x 11 inch)

icing sugar, for sprinkling

low-fat custard or natural yogurt, to serve

1. Melt 15 g/½ oz of the butter in a large frying pan. Add the pears and cook over a low heat for 5 minutes, or until tender. Transfer to a bowl and leave to cool. Gently stir in the blueberries, sugar and ¼ teaspoon of ground cinnamon.

2. Preheat the oven to 180°C/350°F/Gas Mark 4. Place the toast and the remaining cinnamon in a food processor and blend to coarse crumbs. Melt the remaining butter with the oil.

3. Lay one sheet of pastry on a clean work surface and brush lightly with the butter mixture (keep the remaining pastry covered with a damp tea towel while you work to prevent it drying). Sprinkle with one third of the crumbs. Repeat twice more, then cover with the remaining pastry and brush lightly with the butter mixture.

4. Spoon the pear mixture along one long edge and roll up. Press the ends together to seal and transfer to a baking sheet. Brush with the remaining butter mixture and bake in the preheated oven for 40 minutes, or until crisp. Sprinkle with a little icing sugar. Serve warm with custard or yogurt.

Fuller for longer

Vanilla Soufflé Omelettes

 SERVES 4

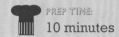 PREP TIME:
10 minutes

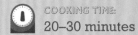 COOKING TIME:
20–30 minutes

nutritional information
per serving

163 kcals, 8g fat, 4.5g sat fat, 8.5g total sugars, 0.5g salt,
2g fibre, 12g carbs, 12g protein

*These fluffy, sweet soufflés look substantial but they
are light as air and low in fat and sugar.*

INGREDIENTS

8 egg whites
2 tbsp clear honey, plus extra for
drizzling
1½ tsp cornflour
2 tsp vanilla extract
250 g/9 oz ricotta cheese
sunflower oil, for brushing
200 g/7 oz raspberries

1. Whisk the egg whites in a large, greasefree bowl until they form
soft peaks.

2. Add the honey, cornflour and vanilla and whisk to mix evenly. Beat
the ricotta in a small bowl until smooth, then fold lightly into the egg
white mixture.

3. Brush a large, heavy-based frying pan with oil and place over a
medium heat. Spoon a quarter of the egg white mixture into the pan
and spread evenly with a palette knife.

4. Cook for 3–4 minutes, or until golden underneath. Turn the omelette
over and cook for 2–3 minutes on the other side then scatter over a
quarter of the raspberries. Gently lift one side with the palette knife
and fold the omelette in half to enclose.

5. Cook for a few seconds more, then flip over onto a serving plate.
Keep warm and repeat with the remaining mixture to make four
omelettes. Serve immediately, drizzled with honey to taste.

1

3

4

SOMETHING
DIFFERENT
For a change of
flavour, omit the
raspberries and
add pecan nuts
instead, then
replace the
honey with
maple syrup.

Peach Popovers

Fuller for longer

Extra low sat fat

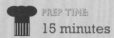 SERVES 4

 PREP TIME:
15 minutes

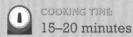 COOKING TIME:
15–20 minutes

nutritional information per serving	167 kcals, 3g fat, 1g sat fat, 11g total sugars, 0.1g salt, 3g fibre, 31g carbs, 6g protein

A good family dessert that is popular with all ages and peaches are also a good source of vitamin C.

INGREDIENTS

1 tsp sunflower oil, plus extra for greasing
100 g/3½ oz plain flour
1 large egg white
250 ml/9 fl oz semi-skimmed milk
1 tsp vanilla extract
3 peaches, sliced
maple syrup, to serve

1. Preheat the oven to 200°C/400°F/Gas Mark 6. Grease 12 holes in a muffin tin.

2. Place the oil, flour, egg white, milk and vanilla in a large bowl. Whisk thoroughly to a smooth, bubbly batter.

3. Place the prepared muffin tin in the preheated oven for 5 minutes. Remove the tin from the oven and quickly divide the peach slices between the holes of the tin and pour the batter evenly into each hole.

4. Bake the popovers for 15–20 minutes, or until well risen, crisp and golden brown.

5. Remove the popovers carefully from the tins with a small palette knife. Serve immediately with maple syrup.

2

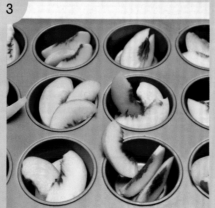

3

3

Red Wine Sorbet

 SERVES 6

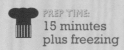 PREP TIME:
15 minutes
plus freezing

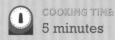 COOKING TIME:
5 minutes

nutritional information per serving	166 kcals, 0g fat, 0g sat fat, 22g total sugars, trace salt, trace fibre, 23g carbs, 1g protein

This fruity sorbet makes the perfect finale to a meal, without too many calories, and is completely fat free!

INGREDIENTS

1 orange

1 lemon

600 ml/1 pint fruity red wine

140 g/5 oz soft light brown sugar

300 ml/10 fl oz water, chilled

2 egg whites, lightly beaten

fresh fruit, to serve

1. Peel the zest from the orange and lemon in strips using a potato peeler, being careful not to remove any of the bitter white pith underneath. Place in a saucepan with the red wine and sugar. Heat gently, stirring until the sugar dissolves, then bring to the boil and simmer for 5 minutes. Remove from the heat and stir in the water.

2. Squeeze the juice from the fruit. Stir into the wine mixture. Cover and leave until completely cooled then strain into a freezerproof container. Cover and freeze for 7–8 hours, or until firm.

3. Working quickly, break the sorbet into chunks and transfer to a food processor. Blend for a few seconds to break down the chunks then, leaving the processor running, gradually pour the egg whites through the feed tube. The mixture will become paler. Continue blending until smooth.

4. Freeze for a further 3–4 hours, or until firm. Scoop into six chilled glasses or dishes and serve immediately with the fresh fruit.

1

2

3

GOES WELL WITH
This sorbet is great with chilled blueberries - buy from the freezer aisle and defrost until still cold.

Fluffy Lemon Pots

 SERVES 4

 PREP TIME:
10 minutes plus standing

COOKING TIME:
5 minutes

nutritional information per serving	77 kcals, 0.8g fat, 0.5g sat fat, 12g total sugars, 0.1g salt, 0g fibre, 13g carbs, 5g protein

Light and fluffy with a refreshing flavour, this simple dessert looks deceptively rich and indulgent.

INGREDIENTS

2 tbsp lemon juice

3 tbsp agave syrup or clear honey

1 mint sprig, plus extra to decorate

2 egg whites

1 tsp finely grated lemon rind

150 g/5½ oz low-fat Greek-style yogurt

1. Place the lemon juice, syrup and mint sprig in a small saucepan over a high heat and bring to the boil, stirring. Remove from the heat and leave to stand for 10 minutes.

2. Meanwhile, place the egg whites in a large, greasefree bowl and whisk with an electric whisk until they hold stiff peaks.

3. Remove the mint from the syrup. Add the lemon rind to the syrup and then gradually drizzle the syrup into the egg whites, whisking at high speed.

4. Add the yogurt to the egg white mixture and fold in lightly with a large metal spoon.

5. Spoon the mixture into four tall glasses or individual pots and top each with a mint sprig. Serve immediately.

1

3

5

Summer Pavlova

 SERVES 6

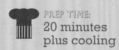 PREP TIME:
20 minutes
plus cooling

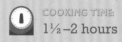 COOKING TIME:
1½–2 hours

nutritional information per serving	110 kcals, 4g fat, 3g sat fat, 11g total sugars, 0.4g salt, 1g fibre, 11g carbs, 3g protein

*This tempting, fruity pavlova is a source of calcium,
and there are antioxidants in the berries.*

INGREDIENTS

meringue
2 egg whites
40 g/1½ oz caster sugar
1 tsp cornflour
1 tsp vanilla extract
1 tsp vinegar

filling
200 g/7 oz low-fat
cream cheese
150 g/5½ oz low-fat natural
yogurt
½–1 tsp vanilla extract,
or to taste
300 g/10½ oz mixed berries

1. Preheat the oven to 120°C/250°F/Gas Mark ½ and line a baking sheet with baking paper. To make the meringue, whisk the egg whites in a large, greasefree bowl until stiff then gradually add the sugar a spoonful at a time, whisking well after each addition. Stir in the cornflour, vanilla extract and the vinegar.

2. When all the sugar has been added and the mixture is stiff, spoon onto the lined baking sheet and form into a 15-cm/6-inch round, hollowing out the centre to form a case.

3. Bake in the preheated oven for 1½–2 hours, or until crisp. Switch the oven off and leave to cool in the oven. Remove from the oven and leave until cold before removing from the baking sheet. Store in an airtight container until required.

4. To make the filling, beat the cream cheese and yogurt together in a bowl until well blended, then stir in the vanilla extract. Clean the fruits, if necessary, and cut any large fruits into bite-sized pieces. When ready to serve, pile the cheese filling in the centre of the pavlova case, top with the fruits and serve, cut into six pieces.

Wheat, gluten
& dairy free

Coconut Rice Pudding with Pomegranate

 SERVES 4

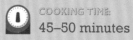 PREP TIME:
15 minutes
plus chilling

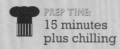 COOKING TIME:
45–50 minutes

nutritional information per serving	154 kcals, 6g fat, 4.5g sat fat, 10g total sugars, trace salt, 1.5g fibre, 21g carbs, 2.5g protein

Creamy-tasting yet dairy-free, this luxurious dessert is fit for any dinner party.

INGREDIENTS

55 g/2 oz pudding rice

200 ml/7 fl oz canned light coconut milk

200 ml/7 fl oz almond milk

25 g/1 oz golden caster sugar

1 cinnamon stick

2 gelatine leaves

1 pomegranate, separated into seeds

grated nutmeg, to sprinkle

4 tbsp pomegranate syrup (optional), to serve

1. Place the rice, coconut milk, almond milk, sugar and cinnamon in a saucepan over a high heat. Bring almost to the boil, stirring, then reduce the heat and cover. Simmer very gently, stirring occasionally, for 40–45 minutes, or until most of the liquid is absorbed.

2. Meanwhile, place the gelatine leaves in a bowl and cover with cold water. Leave to soak for 10 minutes to soften. Drain the leaves, squeezing out any excess moisture, then add to the hot rice mixture and stir lightly until completely dissolved.

3. Spoon the rice mixture into four 150-ml/5-fl oz metal pudding basins, spreading evenly. Leave to cool, then cover and chill in the refrigerator until firm.

4. Run a small knife around the edge of each basin. Dip the bases briefly into a bowl of hot water, then turn out the rice onto four serving plates.

5. Scatter the pomegranate seeds over the rice, then sprinkle with grated nutmeg. Drizzle with a little pomegranate syrup, if using, and serve immediately.

Fuller for longer

Extra low sat fat

Super low calorie

Stuffed Nectarines

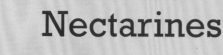 SERVES 4

 PREP TIME:
10 minutes

COOKING TIME:
10 minutes

nutritional information
per serving

93 kcals, 0.2g fat, 0g sat fat, 20g total sugars, 0.1g salt,
4.5g fibre, 16g carbs, 4g protein

An indulgent-tasting dessert that is low in calories and fat and rich in vitamin C, fibre and plant compounds.

INGREDIENTS

4 ripe but firm nectarines or peaches

140 g/5 oz blueberries

115 g/4 oz raspberries

150 ml/5 fl oz freshly squeezed orange juice

1–2 tsp clear honey, or to taste

1 tbsp brandy (optional)

4 tbsp fat-free Greek yogurt

1 tbsp finely grated orange rind

1. Preheat the oven to 180°C/350°F/Gas Mark 4. Cut the nectarines in half, remove the stones then place in a shallow ovenproof dish.

2. Mix the blueberries and raspberries together in a bowl and use to fill the hollows left by the removal of the nectarine stones. Spoon any extra berries around the edge.

3. Mix together the orange juice and honey, and brandy if using, in a small bowl and pour over the fruit. Blend the yogurt with the grated orange rind in another bowl and leave to chill in the refrigerator until required.

4. Bake the berry-filled nectarines in the preheated oven for 10 minutes, or until the fruit is hot. Serve immediately with the orange-flavoured yogurt.

COOK'S NOTE
It's safer to use a
blunt-ended, small
serrated knife for
halving nectarines.
Avoid under-ripe fruit
as it will be hard to
remove the stone.

Golden Polenta Cake

 SERVES 12

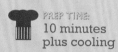 PREP TIME:
10 minutes
plus cooling

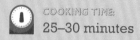 COOKING TIME:
25–30 minutes

nutritional information per serving	125 kcals, 4g fat, 0.7g sat fat, 10g total sugars, 0.19g salt, 0.7g fibre, 20g carbs, 3g protein

Polenta and carrots give this low-fat cake a distinctive texture and rich golden colour.

INGREDIENTS

2 tbsp sunflower oil, plus extra for greasing

100 g/3½ oz light muscovado sugar

finely grated rind of 1 large orange

3 eggs, beaten

200 g/7 oz carrots, roughly grated

100 g/3½ oz quick-cook polenta

40 g/1½ oz gluten-free plain flour blend

1 tsp gluten-free baking powder

syrup

2 tbsp orange juice

1 tbsp clear honey

1. Preheat the oven to 180°C/350°F/Gas Mark 4. Grease a 20-cm/8-inch round deep cake tin and line with baking paper.

2. Whisk together the oil, sugar, orange rind and eggs in a large bowl, until smooth and bubbly. Stir in the carrots. Sift in the polenta, flour and baking powder and fold in evenly.

3. Spoon the mixture into the prepared tin. Bake in the preheated oven for 25–30 minutes, or until just firm to the touch and golden brown. Leave to cool in the tin for 15 minutes.

4. For the syrup, place the orange juice and honey in a small saucepan over a low heat. Heat gently until the honey dissolves, without boiling.

5. Transfer the cake to a wire rack then spoon the syrup evenly over the surface. Leave to cool completely before serving.

GOES WELL WITH
This cake is great when served with low-fat natural yogurt or low-fat crème fraîche.

Apple & Almond Roulade

 SERVES 6

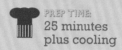 PREP TIME:
25 minutes
plus cooling

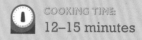 COOKING TIME:
12–15 minutes

nutritional information per serving	184 kcals, 7g fat, 0.6g sat fat, 23.5g total sugars, 0.1g salt, 1.5g fibre, 25g carbs, 6.5g protein

This gluten-free version of a classic roulade is light and luxurious – perfect for entertaining friends.

INGREDIENTS

sunflower oil, for greasing
4 egg whites
100 g/3½ oz golden caster sugar
70 g/2½ oz ground almonds
flaked almonds, to sprinkle
ground cinnamon, to sprinkle

filling

2 red eating apples, such as Gala, cored and chopped
1 tbsp lemon juice
140 g/5 oz low-fat fromage frais

1. Preheat the oven to 200°C/400°F/Gas Mark 6. Grease a 23 x 33-cm/ 9 x 13-inch Swiss roll tin and line with baking paper.

2. Whisk the egg whites in a large, greasefree bowl until stiff enough to hold soft peaks. Whisk in the sugar gradually. Fold in the ground almonds evenly with a large metal spoon.

3. Spread the mixture into the prepared tin and bake in the preheated oven for 12–15 minutes, or until golden brown and firm.

4. Turn the sponge out onto a sheet of baking paper on a clean tea towel and peel off the lining paper. Gently roll up the sponge from one short side, with the clean paper inside. Leave to cool.

5. To make the filling, place the apples in a small saucepan with the lemon juice over a high heat. Bring to the boil, cover and simmer gently, stirring occasionally, for 8–10 minutes, or until tender. Transfer to a food processor or use an electric hand-held blender to process to a rough purée. Leave to cool.

6. Carefully unroll the roulade, remove the paper and spread evenly with the apple mixture. Top with a layer of fromage frais, then roll up loosely to enclose the filling. Sprinkle with almonds and cinnamon and serve in slices.

Extra low sat fat

Super low calorie

Wheat, gluten
& dairy free

Fresh Fruit Salad with Mini Meringues

 SERVES 4

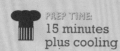 PREP TIME:
15 minutes
plus cooling

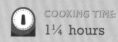 COOKING TIME:
1¼ hours

nutritional information per serving	98 kcals, 0.3g fat, 0.1g sat fat, 18g total sugars, 0.1g salt, 4.5g fibre, 18g carbs, 2.5g protein

A virtually fat-free summer fruits compote, rich in vitamin C with light and airy, low-calorie meringues.

INGREDIENTS

meringues
1 egg white
40 g/1½ oz caster sugar

fruit salad
225 g/8 oz fresh raspberries
2 tsp clear honey
200 ml/7 fl oz water
350 g/12 oz mixed fresh fruits, such as raspberries, strawberries, blackcurrants and stoned cherries
fresh mint sprigs, to garnish

1. Preheat the oven to 120°C/250°F/Gas Mark ½ and line a baking sheet with baking paper.

2. To make the meringues, whisk the egg white in a large, greasefree bowl until stiff then gradually add the sugar a spoonful at a time, whisking well after each addition. When all the sugar has been added and the mixture is stiff, spoon into a piping bag fitted with a large star nozzle and pipe small whirls onto the lined baking sheet. Alternatively, shape into mounds with 2 teaspoons.

3. Bake in the preheated oven for 1 hour, or until crisp. Leave to cool before removing from the baking sheet. Store in an airtight container until required.

4. To make the fruit salad, place the raspberries in a saucepan with the honey and water. Bring to the boil then reduce the heat to a simmer and cook for 5–8 minutes, or until the raspberries have collapsed. Leave to cool for 5 minutes. Transfer to a food processor and process to form a purée.

5. Press the purée through a fine sieve, adding a little extra water if the purée is too thick.

6. Prepare the fresh fruits and stir into the fruit purée. Stir until lightly coated and serve as four portions with the meringues, decorated with a mint sprig.

2

2

5

Fuller for longer

Extra low sat fat

Granola Fruit Pots

 SERVES 4

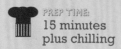 PREP TIME:
15 minutes
plus chilling

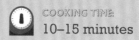 COOKING TIME:
10–15 minutes

nutritional information
per serving

422 kcals, 6g fat, 1g sat fat, 70g total sugars, 0.3g salt,
12g fibre, 80g carbs, 10g protein

Dried fruits are a rich source of fibre and here they're layered with healthy oats and calcium-rich yogurt.

INGREDIENTS

125 g/4½ oz dried apricots
125 g/4½ oz dried prunes
125 g/4½ oz dried peaches
55 g/2 oz dried apples
25 g/1 oz dried cherries
450 ml/16 fl oz unsweetened
apple juice
6 cardamom pods
6 cloves
1 cinnamon stick, broken
300 g/10½ oz low-fat
natural yogurt
115 g/4 oz crunchy oat cereal
fresh fruit, to decorate

1. To make the fruit compote, place the dried apricots, prunes, peaches, apples and cherries in a saucepan and pour in the apple juice.

2. Add the cardamom pods, cloves and cinnamon stick to the pan, bring to the boil and simmer for 10–15 minutes, or until the fruits are plump and tender.

3. Leave the mixture to cool completely in the pan, then transfer the mixture to a bowl and leave to chill in the refrigerator for 1 hour. Remove and discard the spices from the fruits.

4. Spoon the compote into four dessert glasses, layering it alternately with yogurt and oat cereal, finishing with the oat cereal on top.

5. Decorate with fresh fruit and serve immediately.

2

3

4

Fig & Watermelon Salad

 SERVES 4

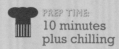 **PREP TIME:**
10 minutes
plus chilling

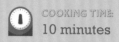 **COOKING TIME:**
10 minutes

nutritional information per serving	196 kcals, 1g fat, 0.5g sat fat, 44g total sugars, trace salt, 1.5g fibre, 43g carbs, 3g protein

Fresh fruits create a stunningly simple dessert that's high in potassium, vitamin C and plant compounds.

INGREDIENTS

1 watermelon, weighing about
1.5 kg/3 lb 5 oz

115 g/4 oz seedless
black grapes

4 figs

syrup dressing
1 lime

grated rind and juice of
1 orange

1 tbsp maple syrup

2 tbsp clear honey

1. Cut the watermelon into quarters and scoop out and discard the seeds. Cut the flesh away from the rind, then chop the flesh into 2.5-cm/1-inch cubes. Place the watermelon cubes in a bowl with the grapes. Cut each fig lengthways into eight wedges and add to the bowl.

2. Grate the lime and mix the rind with the orange rind and juice, maple syrup and honey in a small saucepan. Bring to the boil over a low heat. Pour the mixture over the fruit and stir. Leave to cool. Stir again, cover and chill in the refrigerator for at least 1 hour, stirring occasionally.

3. Divide the fruit salad equally between four bowls and serve.

SOMETHING
DIFFERENT
Instead of
grapes, try
adding the same
weight of fresh
blackberries or
blueberries for
a change.

Stuffed Baked Apples

Fuller for longer

Extra low sat fat

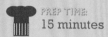 SERVES 4

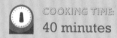 PREP TIME:
15 minutes

COOKING TIME:
40 minutes

| nutritional information per serving | 241 kcals, 5g fat, 0.5g sat fat, 35g total sugars, trace salt, 7g fibre, 43g carbs, 4.5g protein |

There's nothing more comforting than a baked apple and stuffed with plump apricots, ginger and honey, this recipe is a healthy taste sensation.

INGREDIENTS

25 g/1 oz blanched almonds

55 g/2 oz dried apricots

1 piece stem ginger, drained

1 tbsp clear honey

1 tbsp syrup from the stem ginger jar

4 tbsp porridge oats

4 large Bramley apples

1. Preheat the oven to 180°C/350°F/Gas Mark 4. Using a sharp knife, chop the almonds, apricots and stem ginger very finely. Set aside until needed.

2. Place the honey and syrup in a saucepan and heat until the honey has melted. Stir in the oats and cook gently over a low heat for 2 minutes. Remove the saucepan from the heat and stir in the almonds, apricots and stem ginger.

3. Core the apples, widen the tops slightly and score horizontally around the circumference of each to prevent the skins bursting during cooking. Place the apples in a baking dish and fill the cavities with the stuffing. Pour just enough water into the dish to come about one third of the way up the apples. Bake in the preheated oven for 40 minutes, or until tender. Serve immediately.

1

2

3

SOMETHING
DIFFERENT
For a change use
dried cranberries
or mixed fruit
instead of the
apricots.

Blueberry & Honey Yogurt

 SERVES 4   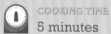 PREP TIME: 15 minutes   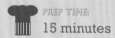 COOKING TIME: 5 minutes

nutritional information per serving	215 kcals, 11g fat, 2g sat fat, 16g total sugars, trace salt, 0.8g fibre, 18g carbs, 9g protein

If you're short of time but still want a tasty dessert, here's a simple and healthy idea that tastes delightful!

INGREDIENTS

3 tbsp clear honey

100 g/3½ oz mixed unsalted nuts

115 g/4 oz low-fat Greek-style yogurt

225 g/8 oz fresh blueberries

1. Heat the honey in a small saucepan over a medium heat. Add the nuts and stir until they are well coated. Remove from the heat and leave to cool slightly.

2. Divide the yogurt between four serving bowls, then spoon the nut mixture over the yogurt, top with the blueberries and serve immediately.

HEALTHY HINT
You could choose
natural bio yogurt
instead of the
Greek yogurt -
the bacteria it
contains can help
beat digestive
troubles.

Fuller for longer

Apple-berry Crumble

 SERVES 8   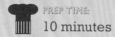 PREP TIME: 10 minutes   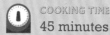 COOKING TIME: 45 minutes

nutritional information per serving | 237 kcals, 7g fat, 4g sat fat, 38g total sugars, 0.4g salt, 4g fibre, 48g carbs, 2g protein

An easy-to-make dessert that is packed with nutrients, our crumble makes a great cold weather treat.

INGREDIENTS

1 spray vegetable oil spray

6 apples, peeled, cored and sliced

70 g/2½ oz dried cranberries or dried cherries

50 g/1¾ oz sugar

½ tsp vanilla extract

topping

60 g/2¼ oz plain flour

100 g/3½ oz soft light brown sugar

½ tsp ground cinnamon

pinch of salt

55 g/2 oz butter, at room temperature

55 g/2 oz porridge oats

1. Preheat the oven to 190°C/375°F/Gas Mark 5. Spray a baking dish with vegetable oil spray.

2. To make the filling, put the apples, dried fruit, sugar and vanilla extract into a medium bowl and toss to mix thoroughly. Spread the mixture in the prepared baking dish, overlapping the apples a little as necessary.

3. To make the topping, combine the flour, brown sugar, cinnamon and salt in the bowl of a food processor or in a large mixing bowl. In the processor, or using two knives, cut the butter into the flour mixture until it resembles coarse breadcrumbs. Stir in the oats.

4. Sprinkle the topping evenly over the filling and bake in the preheated oven for about 45 minutes or until the topping is crisp and beginning to colour. Serve immediately.

2

3

4

Extra low sat fat

Super low calorie

Pineapple Carpaccio with Mango Sauce

 SERVES 4   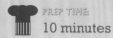 PREP TIME: 10 minutes   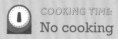 COOKING TIME: No cooking

nutritional information per serving	107 kcals, 0.5g fat, 0.1g sat fat, 24g total sugars, trace salt, 4g fibre, 25g carbs, 2.5g protein

A summery, fresh dessert that is very easy to prepare. Slice the pineapple as thinly as possible.

INGREDIENTS

1 small pineapple
1 ripe mango
juice of ½ lime
100 g/3½ oz fat-free natural yogurt

1. Trim the top and base from the pineapple, then cut off all the skin and remove the 'eyes'. Use a large sharp knife to slice the pineapple into very thin slices. Arrange the slices overlapping on a wide platter.

2. Peel, stone and chop the mango flesh, then sprinkle with lime juice and use a hand-held blender or food processor to process to a smooth purée.

3. Place the mango purée in a small bowl. Spoon in the yogurt and swirl to create a marbled effect.

4. Place the bowl of mango sauce in the centre of the platter. Serve the pineapple with the sauce spooned over.

1

2

3

BE PREPARED
This dessert can be
prepared several hours
in advance. Cover the
sliced pineapple and
sauce with clingfilm
and refrigerate.

Frozen Yogurt Cups

 MAKES 12

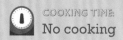 PREP TIME:
10 minutes
plus freezing

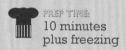 COOKING TIME:
No cooking

nutritional information per cup	26 kcals, 0.4g fat, 0.2g sat fat, 4g total sugars, trace salt, 0.5g fibre, 4g carbs, 2g protein

Packed with calcium and heart-protecting berries, these low-calorie ices are a really tasty treat.

INGREDIENTS

450 g/1 lb low-fat natural yogurt

1½ tbsp finely grated orange rind

225 g/8 oz mixed berries, such as blueberries, raspberries and strawberries, plus extra to decorate

fresh mint sprigs, to decorate (optional)

1. Set the freezer to rapid freeze at least 2 hours before freezing this dish. Line a 12-hole bun tin with 12 paper cake cases, or use small ramekin dishes placed on a baking sheet.

2. Mix the yogurt and orange rind together in a large bowl. Cut any large strawberries into pieces so that they are the same size as the blueberries and raspberries.

3. Add the fruit to the yogurt then spoon into the paper cases or ramekins. Freeze for 2 hours, or until just frozen. Decorate with extra fruit and mint sprigs, if using, and serve. Remember to return the freezer to its original setting afterwards.

SOMETHING
DIFFERENT
You can use lemon rind
instead of the orange if
you like, or a mixture
of both.

Extra low sat fat

Wheat, gluten
& dairy free

Grilled Fruit Kebabs

 SERVES 4

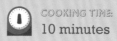 PREP TIME:
10 minutes
plus marinating

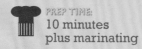 COOKING TIME:
10 minutes

nutritional information per serving	164 kcals, 8g fat, 0.5g sat fat, 22g total sugars, trace salt, 3g fibre, 22g carbs, 1g protein

Apart from small berries, most fruits can be grilled this way. Choose firm fruit so they stay in place.

INGREDIENTS

2 tbsp hazelnut oil

2 tbsp clear honey

juice and finely grated rind of 1 lime

2 pineapple rings, cut into chunks

8 strawberries

1 pear, cored and thickly sliced

1 banana, peeled and thickly sliced

2 kiwi fruit, peeled and quartered

1. Preheat the grill to medium. Mix the oil, honey and lime juice and rind together in a large, shallow, non-metallic dish. Add the fruit and turn to coat. Cover and leave to marinate for 10 minutes.

2. Thread the fruit alternately onto four long metal skewers, beginning with a piece of pineapple and ending with a strawberry.

3. Brush the kebabs with the marinade and cook under the preheated grill, brushing frequently with the marinade, for 5 minutes. Turn the kebabs over, brush with the remaining marinade and grill for a further 5 minutes. Serve immediately.

1

2

3

Extra low sat fat

Wheat, gluten
& dairy free

Pistachio Angel Cake

 SERVES 8

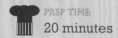 PREP TIME:
20 minutes

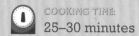 COOKING TIME:
25–30 minutes

nutritional information per serving	170 kcals, 3g fat, 0.3g sat fat, 22g total sugars, 0.1g salt, 0.3g fibre, 32g carbs, 4g protein

This light, gluten-free cake is great when paired with fresh fruit.

INGREDIENTS

sunflower oil, for greasing

6 egg whites

¾ tsp cream of tartar

175 g/6 oz caster sugar

1 tsp vanilla extract

40 g/1½ oz pistachio nuts, finely chopped

85 g/3 oz rice flour, plus extra for dusting

fresh fruit, to serve

1. Preheat the oven to 160°C/325°F/Gas Mark 3. Grease a 1.5-litre/2¾-pint ring tin and dust lightly with a little flour, tipping out the excess.

2. Whisk the egg whites with an electric whisk in a large, greasefree bowl until they hold soft peaks. Stir the cream of tartar into the sugar in a small bowl, then gradually whisk into the egg whites, whisking at high speed until the mixture holds stiff peaks. Whisk in the vanilla.

3. In a separate small bowl, stir the pistachios into the flour. Fold the pistachio mixture into the egg white mixture lightly and evenly using a large metal spoon.

4. Spoon the mixture into the prepared tin and tap the tin to remove any large air bubbles. Bake in the preheated oven for 25–30 minutes, or until golden brown and firm to the touch.

5. Invert the cake onto a wire rack and leave to cool upside down in the tin. When cool, run the tip of a knife around the edges of the cake to loosen, then turn out onto a plate and serve with fresh fruit.

Grilled Cinnamon Oranges

 SERVES 4   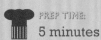 PREP TIME: 5 minutes   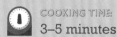 COOKING TIME: 3–5 minutes

nutritional information per serving	88 kcals, 0.2g fat, 0g sat fat, 20g total sugars, trace salt, 3.5g fibre, 20g carbs, 1.5g protein

Fuller for longer

Extra low sat fat

Super low calorie

Wheat, gluten & dairy free

Halved oranges, topped with cinnamon and sugar, will smell absolutely delicious as they grill and are a simple, healthy way to end a meal. They would be equally suited to a breakfast menu too.

INGREDIENTS

4 large oranges
1 tsp ground cinnamon
1 tbsp demerara sugar

1. Preheat the grill to high. Cut the oranges in half and discard any pips. Using a sharp knife carefully cut the flesh away from the skin by cutting around the edge of the fruit. Cut across the segments to loosen the flesh into bite-sized pieces that will then spoon out easily.

2. Arrange the orange halves, cut-side up, in a shallow, flameproof dish. Mix the cinnamon with the sugar in a small bowl and sprinkle evenly over the orange halves.

3. Cook under the preheated grill for 3–5 minutes, until the sugar has caramelized and is golden and bubbling. Serve immediately.

GOES WELL WITH
Top with a low-fat natural yogurt, mixed with honey, for a special treat.

Banana Split Sundae

 SERVES 2

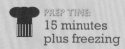 PREP TIME:
15 minutes
plus freezing

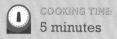 COOKING TIME:
5 minutes

nutritional information per serving	296 kcals, 10g fat, 4.5g sat fat, 45g total sugars, 0.3g salt, 6g fibre, 49g carbs, 9g protein

Sundaes need not be off limits – made using high-fibre banana, this is much lower in fat than you'd expect!

INGREDIENTS

2 small bananas
2 tsp flaked almonds, toasted

chocolate sauce
30 g/1 oz soft light brown sugar
3 tbsp cocoa powder
90 ml/3 fl oz semi-skimmed milk
30 g/1 oz plain chocolate, chopped
½ tsp vanilla extract

1. Peel and dice the bananas, then freeze the diced bananas for 2 hours. In a blender or food processor, process the frozen bananas until creamy. Return the banana purée to the freezer and chill for about 1 hour or until firm.

2. To make the chocolate sauce, put the sugar, cocoa powder and milk in a small saucepan and heat to a simmer over a medium heat. Reduce the heat to low and cook, stirring constantly, for about 1 minute or until the sugar and cocoa powder are dissolved. Remove from the heat and stir in the chopped chocolate until it melts. Stir in the vanilla extract. Leave the sauce to cool slightly.

3. Scoop the banana purée into two bowls, drizzle warm chocolate sauce over the top and sprinkle with the almonds.

SOMETHING
DIFFERENT
Instead of
almonds, use
chopped mixed
nuts, or crushed
walnuts for a
stronger taste.

Fuller for longer

Oaty Plum Bake

 SERVES 4

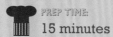 PREP TIME:
15 minutes

 COOKING TIME:
20–25 minutes

nutritional information
per serving

306 kcals, 8g fat, 4g sat fat, 23g total sugars, 0.2g salt,
7.5g fibre, 50g carbs, 7g protein

A healthy variation on a classic crumble. Look for ripe plums as they are naturally sweet.

INGREDIENTS

500 g/1 lb 2 oz ripe red plums,
stoned and quartered
55 g/2 oz low-fat spread
40 g/1½ oz demerara sugar
1 tbsp golden syrup
115 g/4 oz porridge oats
70 g/2½ oz plain wholemeal flour

1. Preheat the oven to 180°C/350°F/Gas Mark 4. Arrange the plums in a 1-litre/1¾-pint baking dish.

2. Place the spread, sugar and syrup in a small saucepan over a low heat. Heat gently, stirring, until the spread is just melted. Remove from the heat and stir in the oats and flour, mixing evenly.

3. Spread the crumble mixture evenly over the plums. Bake in the preheated oven for 20–25 minutes, or until the topping is golden brown and the plums are tender. Serve hot or cold.

1

2

3

GOES WELL WITH
Serve with a
spoonful of low-fat
crème fraîche.

Roasted Vegetables *268*

Raw Beetroot & Pecan Side Salad *270*

Mixed Cabbage Coleslaw *272*

Spicy Pak Choi with Sesame Sauce *274*

Almond French Beans *276*

Hot & Sour Courgettes *278*

Sweet & Sour Red Cabbage *280*

Cauliflower with Lemon & Mustard *282*

Prawn Wonton Baskets *284*

Spiced Basmati Rice *286*

Mexican Rice *288*

Peanut Dip with Pitta Crisps *290*

Sweet Potato Chips *292*

Raw Cashew Hummus *294*

Aubergine Pâté *296*

Fruit, Nut & Seed Grazing Mix *298*

Marshmallow & Cranberry Mini Muffins *300*

Caramel Popcorn Bites *302*

Apple Dip Pots *304*

Beetroot Brownie Bites *306*

Lemon Meringue Biscuits *308*

Maple-nut Granola Bars *310*

Healthy Hot Chocolate *312*

Skinny Strawberry Fizz Cocktail *314*

Sides & Snacks

Roasted Vegetables

Fuller for longer

Extra low sat fat

Super low calorie

Wheat, gluten & dairy free

 SERVES 4

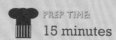 PREP TIME: 15 minutes

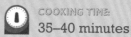 COOKING TIME: 35–40 minutes

nutritional information per serving | 91 kcals, 2.5g fat, 0.5g sat fat, 11g total sugars, trace salt, 6g fibre, 14g carbs, 3g protein

A bright and colourful dish that is crammed with fibre and beneficial plant chemicals.

INGREDIENTS

1 onion, cut into wedges

2–4 garlic cloves, left whole

1 aubergine, about 225 g/ 8 oz, trimmed and cut into cubes

2 courgettes, about 175 g/6 oz, trimmed and cut into chunks

300 g/10½ oz butternut squash, peeled, deseeded and cut into small wedges

2 assorted coloured peppers, deseeded and cut into chunks

2 tsp olive oil

1 tbsp shredded fresh basil

pepper

1. Preheat the oven to 200°C/400°F/Gas Mark 6. Place the onion wedges, whole garlic cloves and aubergine cubes in a large roasting tin.

2. Add the courgettes, squash and peppers to the roasting tin then pour over the oil. Turn the vegetables until they are lightly coated in the oil.

3. Roast the vegetables for 35–40 minutes, or until softened but not mushy. Turn the vegetables over occasionally during cooking.

4. Remove the vegetables from the oven, season with pepper to taste and stir. Scatter with shredded basil and serve immediately.

1

2

4

Raw Beetroot & Pecan Side Salad

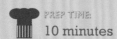 SERVES 4

PREP TIME:
10 minutes

COOKING TIME:
No cooking

nutritional information per serving	121 kcals, 10g fat, 1g sat fat, 5g total sugars, 0.1g salt, 2g fibre, 6g carbs, 1.5g protein

Originally grown just for its leaves, beetroot is a rich source of folic acid and iron.

INGREDIENTS

175 g/6 oz fresh beetroot, roughly grated

8 radishes, thinly sliced

2 spring onions, finely chopped

25 g/1 oz pecan nuts, roughly chopped

8 red chicory leaves or Little Gem lettuce leaves

dressing
2 tbsp extra virgin olive oil

1 tbsp balsamic vinegar

2 tsp creamed horseradish sauce

salt and pepper

1. Combine the beetroot, radishes, spring onions and pecans in a bowl and toss well to mix evenly.

2. Place all the dressing ingredients in a small bowl and whisk lightly with a fork. Season to taste with salt and pepper and pour over the vegetables in the bowl, tossing to coat evenly.

3. Arrange the chicory or lettuce leaves on a serving platter and spoon the salad over them.

4. Serve the salad cold on its own or as an accompaniment to main dishes.

1

2

2

SOMETHING
DIFFERENT
Wrap the salad
in larger lettuce
leaves, such as
cos, to make
parcels for
picnics which
are easier to
transport.

Mixed Cabbage Coleslaw

 SERVES 4

 PREP TIME: 10–15 minutes

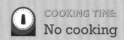 COOKING TIME: No cooking

nutritional information per serving	132 kcals, 0.9g fat, 0.2g sat fat, 26g total sugars, 0.2g salt, 7g fibre, 28g carbs, 3.5g protein

This slaw is ideal with cold chicken or ham and is high in crunch and vitamin C.

INGREDIENTS

85 g/3 oz red cabbage

85 g/3 oz hard white cabbage

55 g/2 oz green cabbage

2 carrots, about 175 g/6 oz, grated

1 onion, finely sliced

2 red apples, cored and chopped

4 tbsp orange juice

2 celery sticks, finely sliced

55 g/2 oz canned sweetcorn kernels

2 tbsp raisins

dressing

4 tbsp low-fat natural yogurt

1 tbsp chopped fresh flat-leaf parsley

pepper

1. Discard the outer leaves and hard central core from the cabbages and shred finely. Wash well in plenty of cold water and drain thoroughly.

2. Place the cabbages in a bowl and stir in the carrots and onion. Toss the apples in the orange juice and add to the cabbages together with any remaining orange juice, and the celery, sweetcorn and raisins. Mix well.

3. For the dressing, mix the yogurt, parsley, and pepper to taste, in a bowl then pour over the cabbage mixture. Stir and serve.

1

2

3

Spicy Pak Choi with Sesame Sauce

 SERVES 4

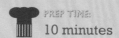 PREP TIME: 10 minutes

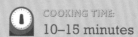 COOKING TIME: 10–15 minutes

nutritional information per serving	163 kcals, 14g fat, 2g sat fat, 4.5g total sugars, 1.7g salt, 3.5g fibre, 4.5g carbs, 4.5g protein

Many of us find leafy greens boring. Well, try this flavour-packed dish... it will change your mind!

INGREDIENTS

2 tsp groundnut or vegetable oil

1 red chilli, deseeded and thinly sliced

1 garlic clove, thinly sliced

5 small pak choi, quartered

100 ml/3½ fl oz vegetable stock

sauce

25 g/1 oz sesame seeds

2 tbsp dark soy sauce

2 tsp soft light brown sugar

1 garlic clove, crushed

3 tbsp sesame oil

1. For the sesame sauce, toast the sesame seeds in a dry frying pan set over a medium heat, stirring until lightly browned. Remove from the heat and cool slightly. Transfer to a pestle and mortar. Add the soy sauce, sugar and crushed garlic and pound to a coarse paste. Stir in the sesame oil.

2. Heat the groundnut oil in a wok or large frying pan. Add the chilli and sliced garlic and stir-fry for 20–30 seconds. Add the pak choi and stir-fry for 5 minutes, adding the stock a little at a time to prevent sticking.

3. Transfer the pak choi to a warmed dish, drizzle the sesame sauce over the top and serve immediately.

GOES WELL WITH
This pak choi tastes great with plain grilled or teriyaki salmon, or stir-fried lean beef or pork strips.

Almond French Beans

 SERVES 4

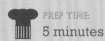 PREP TIME:
5 minutes

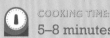 COOKING TIME:
5–8 minutes

nutritional information per serving	156 kcals, 14g fat, 2.5g sat fat, 2.5g total sugars, 0.1g salt, 2.2g fibre, 3g carbs, 4.5g protein

Almonds and beans are a heavenly, healthy combination, and perfect with almost any kind of meat or fish.

INGREDIENTS

300 g/10½ oz French beans, trimmed

1 tbsp sunflower oil

55 g/2 oz flaked almonds

30 g/1 oz low-fat spread

2 tsp lemon juice

2 tbsp finely chopped fresh flat-leaf parsley

salt and pepper

1. Bring a saucepan of lightly salted water to the boil. Add the beans, bring back to the boil and boil for 3–5 minutes, or until tender. Drain well.

2. Meanwhile, heat the oil in a large frying pan over a high heat. Add the almonds and fry, stirring, until golden brown, taking care that they do not burn. Set aside. Use a slotted spoon to transfer the beans to a plate lined with kitchen paper and drain well. Wipe out the frying pan.

3. Melt the spread in the pan. Add the beans and stir. Add the lemon juice, and salt and pepper to taste, then stir in the parsley. Transfer the beans to a serving dish and sprinkle with the almonds to serve.

1

2

3

Low on carbs

Extra low sat fat

Super low calorie

Hot & Sour Courgettes

 SERVES 4

 PREP TIME:
30 minutes

COOKING TIME:
5 minutes

nutritional information per serving	86 kcals, 7g fat, 1.4g sat fat, 4g total sugars, 1.9g salt, 1.1g fibre, 4g carbs, 1.7g protein

In a traditional Sichuan style, this is just one more way to serve the humble courgette.

INGREDIENTS

2 large courgettes, thinly sliced

1 tsp salt

2 tbsp groundnut oil

1 tsp Sichuan peppercorns, crushed

½ –1 red chilli, deseeded and sliced into thin strips

1 large garlic clove, thinly sliced

½ tsp finely chopped fresh ginger

1 tbsp rice vinegar

1 tbsp light soy sauce

2 tsp sugar

1 spring onion, green part included, thinly sliced

a few drops of sesame oil and 1 tsp sesame seeds, to garnish

1. Put the courgette slices in a large colander and toss with the salt. Cover with a plate and put a weight on top. Leave to drain for 20 minutes. Rinse off the salt and spread out the slices on kitchen paper to dry.

2. Preheat a wok over a high heat and add the groundnut oil. Add the Sichuan peppercorns, chilli, garlic and ginger. Fry for about 20 seconds until the garlic is just beginning to colour.

3. Add the courgette slices and toss in the oil. Add the rice vinegar, soy sauce and sugar, and stir-fry for 2 minutes. Add the spring onion and fry for 30 seconds. Garnish with the sesame oil and seeds, and serve immediately.

1

2

3

Sweet & Sour Red Cabbage

Fuller for longer

Extra low sat fat

Super low calorie

 SERVES 6

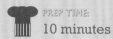 PREP TIME: 10 minutes

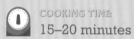 COOKING TIME: 15–20 minutes

nutritional information per serving	102 kcals, 3g fat, 0.5g sat fat, 16.3g total sugars, trace salt, 4.5g fibre, 17g carbs, 1.5g protein

We've boosted the flavour and reduced the fat in this dish, which is a great accompaniment to lean roast pork.

INGREDIENTS

1 red cabbage, about 750 g/1 lb 10 oz

2 tbsp olive oil

2 onions, finely sliced

1 garlic clove, chopped

2 small cooking apples, peeled, cored and sliced

2 tbsp muscovado sugar

½ tsp ground cinnamon

1 tsp crushed juniper berries

whole nutmeg, for grating

2 tbsp red wine vinegar

grated rind and juice of 1 orange

2 tbsp redcurrant jelly

salt and pepper

1. Cut the cabbage into quarters, remove the centre stalk and finely shred the leaves.

2. Heat the oil in a large saucepan over a medium heat and add the cabbage, onions, garlic and apples. Stir in the sugar, cinnamon and juniper berries and grate a quarter of the nutmeg into the pan.

3. Pour over the vinegar and orange juice and add the orange rind.

4. Stir well and season to taste with salt and pepper. The pan will be quite full but the volume of the cabbage will reduce during cooking.

5. Cook over a medium heat, stirring occasionally, until the cabbage is just tender but still firm to the bite. This will take 10–15 minutes, depending on how finely the cabbage is sliced.

6. Stir in the redcurrant jelly, then taste and adjust the seasoning, adding salt and pepper if necessary. Serve immediately.

2

3

6

BE PREPARED
You can make this in advance and store it in a lidded container in the fridge for up to a day before serving.

Low on carbs

Fuller for longer

Extra low sat fat

Super low calorie

Cauliflower with Lemon & Mustard

 SERVES 4

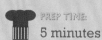 PREP TIME:
5 minutes

 COOKING TIME:
6–8 minutes

nutritional information per serving	68 kcals, 4g fat, 0.6g sat fat, 3g total sugars, 0.2g salt, 3g fibre, 3.5g carbs, 4.5g protein

Instead of masking the delicate flavour of cauliflower in cheese sauce, try this lighter alternative.

INGREDIENTS

1 cauliflower, about 450 g/1 lb, cut into florets
1 tbsp olive oil
1 tbsp wholegrain mustard
finely grated rind of 1 lemon
salt and pepper

1. Place the cauliflower florets in a steamer over a saucepan of gently boiling water. Cover and steam for 6–8 minutes, or until almost tender. Drain the cauliflower well.

2. Whisk the oil, mustard and lemon rind with a fork in a small bowl until combined. Stir the dressing into the cauliflower, gently turning to coat evenly. Season to taste with salt and pepper.

3. Tip the cauliflower into a warm serving dish and serve immediately, as a side dish.

1

2

2

GOES WELL WITH
This very tasty, lemony cauliflower goes really well with grilled fish.

Prawn Wonton Baskets

 SERVES 4

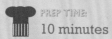 PREP TIME:
10 minutes

 COOKING TIME:
4–5 minutes

nutritional information per serving | 146 kcals, 9g fat, 1.5g sat fat, 1g total sugars, 0.9g salt, 2g fibre, 8g carbs, 8g protein

These crunchy little cups are great for a savoury snack or a party canapé that won't break your diet.

INGREDIENTS

sesame oil, for greasing and brushing
12 wonton wrappers
1 ripe avocado
1 tbsp lime juice
150 g/5½ oz cooked, peeled prawns
1 tbsp snipped fresh chives
1 tsp soy sauce
pepper
sesame seeds, to serve

1. Preheat the oven to 200°C/400°F/Gas Mark 6. Grease 12 holes in a muffin tin.

2. Press wonton wrappers into the prepared holes in the tin, then brush with sesame oil. Bake in the preheated oven for 4–5 minutes, or until crisp and golden. Leave to cool on a wire rack.

3. Meanwhile, halve the avocado, remove the stone and scoop out the flesh. Cut into small dice, sprinkle with lime juice, and mix with the prawns and chives in a bowl. Season to taste with pepper.

4. Spoon the avocado mixture into the wonton cups and splash the tops with soy sauce. Sprinkle with sesame seeds just before serving.

2

3

4

BE PREPARED
If you are making these for a party, prepare to the end of step 3 earlier in the day, chill the filling and assemble before serving.

Spiced Basmati Rice

Fuller for longer

Extra low sat fat

Wheat, gluten & dairy free

 SERVES 4

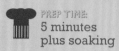 PREP TIME: 5 minutes plus soaking

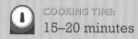 COOKING TIME: 15–20 minutes

nutritional information per serving	260 kcals, 6.5g fat, 3g sat fat, 0g total sugars, 1.5g salt, trace fibre, 42g carbs, 4g protein

Basmati rice has a lower glycaemic index than other types of carb, and this dish is packed with flavour too.

INGREDIENTS

225 g/8 oz basmati rice

2 tbsp vegetable oil or groundnut oil

5 green cardamom pods, bruised

5 cloves

½ cinnamon stick

1 tsp fennel seeds

½ tsp black mustard seeds

2 bay leaves

450 ml/16 fl oz water

1½ tsp salt, or to taste

pepper

1. Rinse the rice in several changes of water until the water runs clear, then leave to soak for 30 minutes. Drain and set aside until ready to cook.

2. Heat a casserole or large saucepan with a tight-fitting lid over a medium–high heat, then add the oil. Add the spices and bay leaves and stir for 30 seconds. Stir the rice into the casserole so the grains are coated with oil. Stir in the water and salt and bring to the boil.

3. Reduce the heat to as low as possible and cover the casserole tightly. Simmer, without lifting the lid, for 8–10 minutes, until the grains are tender and all the liquid has been absorbed.

4. Turn off the heat and use two forks to mix the rice. Season to taste with pepper. Re-cover the pan and leave to stand for 5 minutes before serving.

1

2

4

HEALTHY HINT
Groundnut oil is higher
in healthier types of fat
than other oils, so use
this if you can find it.

Extra low sat fat

Mexican Rice

 SERVES 4   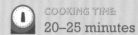 PREP TIME: 10 minutes   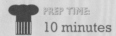 COOKING TIME: 20–25 minutes .

nutritional information per serving	209 kcals, 0.7g fat, 0.1g sat fat, 4g total sugars, trace salt, 2g fibre, 42g carbs, 5g protein

A simple and tasty low-fat rice dish which makes a great accompaniment for grilled chicken.

INGREDIENTS

1 onion, chopped

400 g/14 oz plum tomatoes, peeled, deseeded and chopped

250 ml/9 fl oz vegetable stock

200 g/7 oz long-grain rice

salt and pepper

1. Put the onion and tomatoes in a food processor and process to a smooth purée. Scrape the purée into a saucepan, pour in the stock and bring to the boil over a medium heat, stirring occasionally.

2. Add the rice and stir once, then reduce the heat, cover and simmer for 20–25 minutes, or until all the liquid has been absorbed and the rice is tender. Season to taste with salt and pepper and serve immediately.

SOMETHING DIFFERENT

Spice up this Mexican rice dish by adding some chopped fresh chillies, garlic and coriander at the start of step 2.

Peanut Dip with Pitta Crisps

 SERVES 6   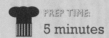 PREP TIME: 5 minutes   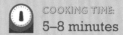 COOKING TIME: 5–8 minutes

nutritional information per serving	280 kcals, 17g fat, 3g sat fat, 2.5g total sugars, 1g salt, 3g fibre, 21g carbs, 10g protein

Rich in protein, peanut butter is a useful storecupboard standby for easy sweet or savoury snacks.

INGREDIENTS

175 g/6 oz crunchy peanut butter

1 small red chilli, deseeded and finely chopped

2 tsp dark soy sauce

juice of 1 lime

3–4 tbsp water

4 small pitta breads

sesame oil, for spraying

1 tbsp sesame seeds

salt and pepper

1. Place the peanut butter, chilli, soy sauce and lime juice in a saucepan over a low heat. Cook gently without boiling, stirring, until evenly mixed. Stir in just enough water to make a soft paste. Season to taste with salt and pepper. Set aside and keep warm.

2. Preheat a grill to high. Slice the pittas into strips about 2 cm/¾ inch wide and arrange in a single layer on a baking sheet. Spray lightly with sesame oil and sprinkle with the sesame seeds.

3. Grill the pittas for 2–3 minutes, turning once, until golden and crisp.

4. Spoon the peanut dip into a small bowl and serve warm, with the pitta crisps on the side for dipping.

1

1

2

HEALTHY HINT
For an extra
healthy snack,
replace the
pittas with raw
vegetable crudités,
such as sticks
of carrot and
celery.

Fuller for longer

Extra low sat fat

Wheat, gluten & dairy free

Sweet Potato Chips

 SERVES 4

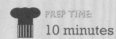 PREP TIME: 10 minutes

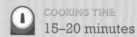 COOKING TIME: 15–20 minutes

nutritional information per serving	202 kcals, 1.5g fat, 0.5g sat fat, 12g total sugars, 0.7g salt, 7g fibre, 48g carbs, 3g protein

You'll absolutely love these low-fat, vitamin-C rich sweet potato chips as a change from potato chips.

INGREDIENTS

2 sprays vegetable oil spray
900 g/2 lb sweet potatoes
½ tsp salt
½ tsp ground cumin
¼ tsp cayenne pepper

1. Preheat the oven to 230°C/450°F/Gas Mark 8. Spray a large baking sheet with vegetable oil spray.

2. Peel the sweet potatoes and slice into 5-mm/¼-inch thick spears about 7.5 cm/3 inches long. Spread the sweet potatoes on the prepared baking sheet and spray them with vegetable oil spray.

3. In a small bowl, combine the salt, cumin and cayenne. Sprinkle the spice mixture evenly over the sweet potatoes and then toss to coat.

4. Spread the sweet potatoes out into a single layer and bake in the preheated oven for about 15–20 minutes, or until cooked through and lightly coloured. Serve hot.

2

2

2

SOMETHING DIFFERENT

Instead of the salt, cumin and cayenne, you could use 1¼ tsp Cajun seasoning.

Low on carbs

Fuller for longer

Raw Cashew Hummus

 SERVES 5

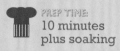 PREP TIME:
10 minutes
plus soaking

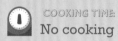 COOKING TIME:
No cooking

nutritional information per serving	288 kcals, 29g fat, 4.8g sat fat, 1.4g total sugars, trace salt, 2g fibre, 5.2g carbs, 6.4g protein

This nut dish has all the flavour of a good hummus – but is also very high in protein and good fats.

INGREDIENTS

150 g/5½ oz cashew nuts
2 tbsp tahini
juice of 2 lemons
4 tbsp olive oil
½ tsp onion powder
½ tsp garlic powder
sea salt and pepper
paprika and chilli oil, to serve
toasted pitta breads,
to serve

1. Soak the cashew nuts in a bowl of water for 2 hours.

2. Drain the cashews and place them in a blender or food processor with the tahini, lemon juice, olive oil, onion powder and garlic powder. Process to a smooth paste. Gradually add a little water to adjust the consistency to suit your preference. Taste and adjust the seasoning with salt and pepper.

3. Transfer to a small dish and serve with a dusting of paprika, a drizzle of chilli oil and the toasted pitta breads.

1

2

2

HEALTHY HINT
Don't use salted
cashews for this
dish, buy the
raw unsalted
type and increase
the fibre content
with wholemeal
pittas.

Aubergine Pâté

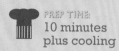 SERVES 6

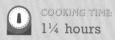 PREP TIME:
10 minutes
plus cooling

COOKING TIME:
1¼ hours

nutritional information per serving	73 kcals, 7.5g fat, 1g sat fat, 1g total sugars, trace salt, 1.3g fibre, 8g carbs, 1.4g protein

This is also known as Poor Man's Caviar because the humble aubergine tastes so delicious in this recipe!

INGREDIENTS

2 large aubergines

4 tbsp extra virgin olive oil

2 garlic cloves,
very finely chopped

4 tbsp lemon juice

salt and pepper

2 tbsp roughly chopped fresh
flat-leaf parsley, to garnish

6 crisp breads, to serve

1. Preheat the oven to 180°C/350°F/Gas Mark 4. Score the skins of the aubergines with the point of a sharp knife, without piercing the flesh, and place them on a baking sheet. Bake for 1¼ hours, or until soft.

2. Remove the aubergines from the oven and leave until cool enough to handle. Cut them in half and, using a spoon, scoop out the flesh into a bowl. Mash the flesh thoroughly.

3. Gradually beat in the olive oil then stir in the garlic and lemon juice. Season to taste with salt and pepper. Cover with clingfilm and store in the refrigerator until required. Sprinkle with the parsley and serve with crisp breads.

1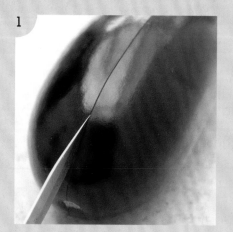

2

3

COOK'S NOTE
This makes a great
dip too, served with
sticks of carrot, celery
and pepper.

Fruit, Nut & Seed Grazing Mix

Low on carbs

Fuller for longer

Extra low sat fat

Super low calorie

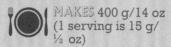 MAKES 400 g/14 oz (1 serving is 15 g/½ oz)

 PREP TIME: 10 minutes

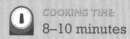 COOKING TIME: 8–10 minutes

nutritional information per serving | 75 kcals, 6g fat, 0.5g sat fat, 1g total sugars, trace salt, 1g fibre, 2.5g carbs, 2.5g protein

A crunchy snack that is good to nibble on during the day to keep hunger pangs at bay.

INGREDIENTS

200 g/7 oz whole unblanched almonds

25 g/1 oz pine nuts

25 g/1 oz pumpkin seeds

25 g/1 oz sunflower seeds

25 g/1 oz dried banana chips

55 g/2 oz dates, stoned and roughly chopped

2 tbsp oat bran

½ tsp ground mixed spice

1 small egg white

1. Preheat the oven to 200°C/400°F/Gas Mark 6. Combine the almonds, pine nuts, pumpkin and sunflower seeds, banana chips, dates, oat bran and spice in a large bowl and mix well.

2. Lightly beat the egg white with a fork in a small bowl, then add to the nut mixture in the bowl, stirring to coat all the ingredients evenly.

3. Spread the mixture out on a large baking sheet in a single layer. Bake in the preheated oven for 8–10 minutes, or until crisp and lightly browned.

4. Leave to cool completely before serving or pack into an airtight container and consume within 5 days.

SOMETHING
DIFFERENT
For a more savoury
mix, omit the bananas
and dates and replace
the spice with 1 tsp
mild curry powder
and 1/4 tsp salt.

Marshmallow & Cranberry Mini Muffins

 MAKES 48

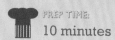 PREP TIME: 10 minutes

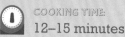 COOKING TIME: 12–15 minutes

nutritional information per muffin	38 kcals, 1g fat, 0.1g sat fat, 2g total sugars, 0.1g salt, 0.3g fibre, 6g carbs, 0.7g protein

These tasty little low-fat muffins are bite-sized so they are just enough to satisfy sweet cravings.

INGREDIENTS

200 g/7 oz plain flour

1 tbsp baking powder

85 g/3 oz light muscovado sugar

100 g/3½ oz dried cranberries

25 g/1 oz mini marshmallows

finely grated rind of ½ small lemon

1 tbsp lemon juice

1 egg, beaten

100 ml/3½ fl oz skimmed milk

3 tbsp sunflower oil

½ tsp vanilla extract

1. Preheat the oven to 200°C/400°F/Gas Mark 6. Place 48 mini muffin cases on two or three baking sheets or in mini muffin tins.

2. Sift together the flour, baking powder and sugar in a bowl. Stir in the cranberries and marshmallows.

3. Whisk together lemon rind and juice, egg, milk, oil and vanilla in a bowl then stir into the dry ingredients to make a soft batter.

4. Spoon the batter into the mini muffin cases and bake in the preheated oven for 12–15 minutes, or until risen, firm and golden. Transfer to a wire rack to cool before serving.

2

3

4

Extra low sat fat

Caramel Popcorn Bites

 SERVES 8   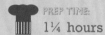 PREP TIME: 1¼ hours   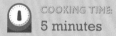 COOKING TIME: 5 minutes

nutritional information per serving	230 kcals, 7.5g fat, 2.5g sat fat, 38g total sugars, 1.3g salt, trace fibre, 44g carbs, 0.7g protein

Popcorn is one of the lowest calorie snacks you can choose, and our quick recipe is really special.

INGREDIENTS

100 g/3½ oz sugar
110 g/3¾ oz soft light brown sugar
125 ml/4 fl oz golden syrup
25 g/1 oz butter
1½ tsp bicarbonate of soda
1 tsp salt
½ tsp vanilla extract
80 g/2¾ oz plain, air-popped popcorn

1. Cover a large baking sheet with baking paper or kitchen foil.

2. In a saucepan, combine the sugars, golden syrup and butter and bring to the boil over a medium–high heat. Reduce the heat to medium and boil, without stirring, for 4 minutes. Carefully stir in the bicarbonate of soda, salt and vanilla extract.

3. Put the popcorn in a large mixing bowl. Pour the caramel over the popcorn and stir to coat. Using two spoons, form the mixture into 24 balls, about 5 cm/2 inches in diameter, and place them on the lined baking sheet. Leave to sit at room temperature for about 1 hour or until firm. Serve at room temperature.

2

3

3

Apple Dip Pots

Fuller for longer

Extra low sat fat

Super low calorie

 SERVES 4

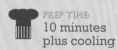 PREP TIME:
10 minutes
plus cooling

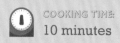 COOKING TIME:
10 minutes

nutritional information
per serving

106 kcals, 0.5g fat, 0.2g sat fat, 23g total sugars, trace salt,
4g fibre, 24g carbs, 2.4g protein

A high fibre, low glycaemic index snack with no added sugar so they are good for a lunchbox surprise.

INGREDIENTS

4 sweet eating apples

finely grated rind and
juice of 1 orange

150 g/5½ oz low-fat
natural yogurt

1. Thinly peel, core and roughly chop two of the apples and place in a saucepan with the orange rind and about two thirds of the juice over a low heat. Heat gently until boiling, then cover and simmer gently, stirring occasionally, for 6–8 minutes, to soften.

2. Remove from the heat and process with an electric hand-held blender or in a food processor until smooth. Leave to cool completely.

3. Core the remaining two apples and cut into thick slices. Toss the slices in the remaining orange juice to prevent browning.

4. Stir the yogurt lightly into the apple purée in a small bowl. Serve in small pots or bowls, with the apple slices on the side for dipping.

HEALTHY HINT
For a dairy-free
version, you can
omit the yogurt
or simply
replace it with
soya yogurt.

Beetroot Brownie Bites

 MAKES 36   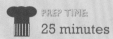 PREP TIME: 25 minutes   COOKING TIME: 25–30 minutes

nutritional information per bite

75 kcals, 4g fat, 1.5g sat fat, 7g total sugars, trace salt, 0.5g fibre, 10g carbs, 1.5g protein

Dark chocolate and beetroot are rich in antioxidants, so these gooey treats are not as wicked as they look.

INGREDIENTS

150 g/5½ oz plain dark chocolate, broken into small pieces

2 eggs

1 tsp vanilla extract

150 g/5½ oz dark muscovado sugar

85 ml/3 fl oz sunflower oil, plus extra for greasing

225 g/8 oz cooked beetroot, grated

100 g/3½ oz self-raising flour

3 tbsp cocoa powder

1. Preheat the oven to 180°C/350°F/Gas Mark 4. Lightly grease a 20-cm/8-inch square baking tin and line with baking paper.

2. Place the chocolate in a heatproof bowl, set over a pan of gently simmering water and heat until just melted. Remove from the heat.

3. Place the eggs, vanilla and sugar in a bowl and whisk at high speed with an electric whisk for 3–4 minutes, or until pale and frothy. Beat in the oil. Stir in the beetroot, then sift over the flour and cocoa and fold in. Add the melted chocolate and stir evenly.

4. Spoon the mixture into the prepared tin and bake in the preheated oven for 25–30 minutes, or until just firm to the touch. Leave to cool in the tin, then turn out and leave to cool completely on a wire rack.

5. Cut into about 36 bite-sized squares and serve.

2

3

3

FREEZING TIP
Pack the brownies
into an airtight
freezer container,
seal, label and
freeze for up
to 3 months.
Thaw at room
temperature.

Extra low sat fat

Super low calorie

Wheat, gluten & dairy free

Lemon Meringue Biscuits

 SERVES 8

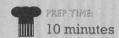 PREP TIME: 10 minutes

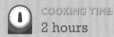 COOKING TIME: 2 hours

nutritional information **per serving**

73 kcals, 0g fat, 0g sat fat, 17g total sugars, 0.3g salt, 0g fibre, 18g carbs, 0.7g protein

A fat-free, low-calorie treat, ideal for a mid-afternoon break with a hot drink.

INGREDIENTS

2 large egg whites
⅛ tsp cream of tartar
pinch of salt
140 g/5 oz sugar
finely grated zest of 1 lemon

1. Preheat the oven to 110°C/225°F/Gas Mark ¼. Line a large baking sheet with foil or baking paper.

2. In a large, greasefree bowl, beat the egg whites with an electric mixer on high speed until they are frothy. Add the cream of tartar and salt and continue to beat on high until soft peaks form. Gradually add the sugar and continue to beat on high for about 3–4 minutes or until stiff peaks form. Fold in the lemon zest.

3. Drop the batter in rounded teaspoons onto the prepared baking sheet. Bake in the preheated oven for about 1½ hours or until dry and crisp but not yet beginning to colour. Turn off the oven and leave the biscuits inside the oven for a further 30 minutes. Serve at room temperature.

2

2

3

BE PREPARED
Meringues store well
in an airtight container
for several weeks or
more - so make them in
advance for unexpected
guests!

Extra low sat fat

Maple-nut Granola Bars

 MAKES 12

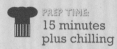 PREP TIME:
15 minutes
plus chilling

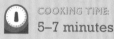 COOKING TIME:
5–7 minutes

nutritional information per bar	200 kcals, 10g fat, 1.5g sat fat, 11g total sugars, 0.2g salt, 2g fibre, 22.8g carbs, 5g protein

These granola bars have all the flavour of a flapjack, but are packed with healthy nuts and seeds.

INGREDIENTS

1 spray vegetable oil spray
165 g/5¾ oz porridge oats
50 g/1¾ oz pecan nuts, chopped
50 g/1¾ oz flaked almonds
120 ml/3¾ fl oz maple syrup
50 g/1¾ oz soft light brown sugar
60 g/2¼ oz smooth peanut butter
1 tsp vanilla extract
¼ tsp salt
30 g/1 oz puffed rice cereal
30 g/1 oz ground linseeds

1. Preheat the oven to 180°C/350°F/Gas Mark 4. Coat a 23 x 33-cm/ 9 x 13-inch baking tin with vegetable oil spray.

2. On a separate large, rimmed baking tray, combine the oats, pecan nuts and almonds and toast in the preheated oven for 5–7 minutes or until lightly browned.

3. Meanwhile, combine the maple syrup, brown sugar and peanut butter in a small saucepan and bring to the boil over a medium heat. Cook, stirring, for about 4–5 minutes or until the mixture thickens slightly. Stir in vanilla extract and salt.

4. When the oats and nuts are toasted, place them in a mixing bowl and add the rice cereal and linseeds. Add the syrup mixture to the oat mixture and stir to combine. Spread the syrup-oat mixture into the prepared baking tin and chill for at least 1 hour before cutting into 12 bars. Store in a tightly covered container at room temperature. Serve at room temperature.

Fuller for longer

Extra low sat fat

Healthy Hot Chocolate

 SERVES 1

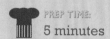 PREP TIME:
5 minutes

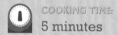 COOKING TIME:
5 minutes

nutritional information per serving	260 kcals, 4g fat, 2g sat fat, 29g total sugars, 0.9g salt, 5g fibre, 48g carbs, 12g protein

Cocoa can help lower blood pressure and improve cholesterol levels while skimmed milk is calcium rich.

INGREDIENTS

1 tbsp sugar

2 tbsp cocoa powder

pinch of ground cinnamon (optional)

225 ml/8 fl oz skimmed milk

¼ tsp vanilla extract

1 large marshmallow

1. In a small saucepan, combine the sugar, cocoa powder, cinnamon (if using) and about 2 tablespoons of the milk. Stir to make a paste.

2. Add the remaining milk and heat to a simmer over a medium heat. Cook, stirring occasionally, for about 3 minutes until the cocoa and sugar are completely dissolved.

3. Stir in vanilla extract and serve immediately, topped with a marshmallow.

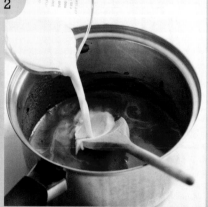

SOMETHING
DIFFERENT
For a special winter
treat, add a sprinkling
of nutmeg over the top
of the hot chocolate.

Skinny Strawberry Fizz Cocktail

 SERVES 4

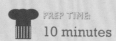 PREP TIME: 10 minutes

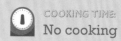 COOKING TIME: No cooking

nutritional information per serving	93 kcals, 0g fat, 0g sat fat, 8.5g total sugars, trace salt, 0.8g fibre, 9g carbs, 0.5g protein

Cocktails can be high in calories, but this one allows you to have the occasional guilt-free tipple.

INGREDIENTS

200 g/7 oz strawberries, hulled
2 tbsp agave syrup
juice of 1 lime
8 tbsp crushed ice
100 ml/4 fl oz vodka
400 ml/14 fl oz diet cola
whole strawberries and strips of lime zest, to decorate

1. Place the strawberries, syrup and lime in a plastic jug and process with an electric hand-held blender or in a food processor until smooth.

2. Add 2 tablespoons of crushed ice to each of four tall glasses.

3. Pour the strawberry mixture evenly into each glass, add 25 ml/ 1 fl oz of vodka to each glass and stir to mix.

4. Top up the glasses with the cola to taste, place a strawberry and strips of lime zest on the rims, and serve immediately.

1

3

4

Index